ENVIRONMENTAL I

the **Global**
CONSEQUENCES

is tu

David Money

Hodder & Stoughton

A MEMBER OF THE HODDER HEADLINE GROUP

Acknowledgements

The author and publishers thank the following for permission to reproduce photographs in this book.

J Allan Cash p.89 bottom right; Metropolitan Toronto Reference Library p.5 bottom right; Rex features p.11 centre; Robert Harding p.45 top right, p.67 bottom right, p.87 bottom left, p.89 bottom left; Sylvia Cordaiy Photo Library p.65 bottom right, p.71 bottom right, p.85 top.

All other photos belong to the author.

Every effort has been made to trace and acknowledge correctly all copyright holders but if any have been overlooked the publishers will be pleased to make the necessary arrangements at the first opportunity.

Cover photographs

Top left • Pressure on the environment by people with limited resources, reflected in Yunnan, south-west China, by the intensive cultivation of a fertile vale bordered by drastic erosion of hillsides unwisely denuded of vegetation.

Bottom left • An industrially developed country imports wheat produced by the mechanical cultivation of extensive temperate grasslands.

Top right • Winnowing in the Ethiopian highland where a bare sufficiency of grain has long been at the mercy of climatic vagaries and unstable political regimes.

Bottom right • Industrial environmental pollution north of Naples – an urban sprawl extending over a formerly productive rural landscape adjoining the Phlegrean Fields.

Cataloguing in Publication Data is available from the British Library

ISBN 0 340 609893

First published 1994
Impression number 10 9 8 7 6 5 4 3 2 1
Year   1998 1997 1996 1995 1994

Typeset by Litho Link Ltd., Welshpool Powys, Wales
Printed in Hong Kong for Hodder & Stoughton Educational, a division of Hodder Headline Plc, 338 Euston Road, London NW1 3BH by Colorcraft Limited.

CONTENTS

Part 5 The ever-increasing population

References

1 (p.8) King J W (1973) "Solar radiation changes and the weather", *Nature* 245 p.445

2 (p.8) Lamb H H (1982) "Climatic change", *Geography* 67 (3) p.206

3 (p.22) Innes J (1991) "Measuring effects of atmospheric pollution on trees in Europe", *Geography* 76 (1) p.70

4 (p.34) UNDP (1989) Bangladesgh flood policy study. Final Report. (Dhaka)

5 (p.35) Brammar H (1990) "Floods in Bangladesh", *Geographical Journal* 156 (2) pp.158-165

6 (p.50) Binns J A (1990) "Is Desertification a Myth?", *Geography* 15 (2) pp.106-113

7 (p.50) Goudie A (1991) "The climatic sensitivity of desert margins", *Geography* 76 (1) p.73

8 (p.77) Reddy A KN and Goldemberg J (1990) "Energy consumption", *Scientific American* 262

PREFACE

The importance of a balanced view

It becomes increasingly evident that many environmental disturbances have world-wide consequences and that some, such as induced climatic change, may affect future generations. These concern us all. Nevertheless a purely emotional response may lead to hasty decisions, wrong priorities, the waste of resources, and possible neglect of more important issues. It can also be exploited: a 'doom and gloom' approach and 'shock-horror' description sells newspapers, and 'environmentally-friendly' and 'green' may be used to describe products which are not necessarily so. It may be argued that this makes people aware that there *are* problems, and this is indeed so. However, there is also the danger that those who have not considered a problem in depth, nor in proper perspective, may exert unwise pressures. A concerned but enquiring approach is likely to be of greater benefit in the long term and make for suitably sensible precautions.

With any environmental problem there are almost always a number of contributing causes, whose interactions and feedbacks make it difficult to identify the most effective course of action and predict the consequences of intended remedies with any certainty. While we can't expect to appreciate all the feedback mechanisms between earth's organisms and their environment, the Gaia hypothesis suggests that, overall, these interact so as to enable our global system to function for its long-term benefit. If so, it is possible that as we continue to disturb our environment these may interact to exclude *us* – for the general good of the system!

It is tempting for a layman to accept the opinion of a certain investigator, researcher, or publicist as established fact; yet, simply because environmental issues *are* apt to be complex, experts frequently disagree about the seriousness of a hazard, its potential consequences, and the best way to counter it.

Here various environmental issues of current concern are examined in turn, and are seen to be interlinked by flows of energy through the atmosphere, oceans, lithosphere, and biosphere – the latter, of course, including the ever-increasing human population with its varying levels of technology. In each case the possible reasons for environmental disturbance and the likely consequences are considered: virtually every issue emphasises that contributing causes frequently conflict and that feedbacks make forecasting hazardous.

The lay-out enables particular issues to be selected for consideration and discussion. Some causes are common to a number of environmental disturbances, and are therefore re-examined, at an appropriate depth, in various parts of the book.

ENERGY – THE KEY TO IT ALL

Flows of energy are involved in every environmental problem – whether global warming, ozone depletion or population pressure on resources. Energy is indestructible but exists in many interchangeable forms (for example electric energy is transformed in a filament to heat and light energy).

The sun continuously supplies energy to the planet, to its atmosphere and everything at the surface, though with small but significant variations in the amount emitted. Some is returned directly and about twice as much is lost to space from within the global system, the total loss approximately balancing the solar energy received (I.2).

Within the global system energy flows are continuous. Solar energy heats the earth's surface, which warms the air above, providing energy for movement – wind which impels oceans surfaces, whose currents transfer large amounts of energy about the globe. The sun's energy releases water vapour from the oceans, which on condensation transfers heat energy to the air. The moving air supplies moisture to plants, and they use solar energy to create material for their roots, stems, leaves and fruit. These are substances which feed animals, and they in turn use the energy received in numerous ways. Our demands for food energy lead to agricultural practices which affect the environment. Our use of fossil fuels derived from plant and animal remains release undesirable chemicals and energy to the atmosphere.

Energy stored and released

Energy remains latent for short periods in plants, and for a very long time in fossil fuels. The oceans, too, are great reservoirs of energy. Earth's own reserves of geothermal energy can be environmentally disturbing when released through volcanic action but, like that stored in atoms of radioactive materials, they can be tapped for our own purposes. The planet's energy of movement, its spin, and gravitational force influence flows of air and water, whose energy we harness. Yet the sun remains the prime source of the energy flowing within our global system.

The nature of energy exchanges

All bodies radiate energy of various wavelengths. Electromagnetic radiation from the sun travels through space as photons of energy. Almost all of that reaching earth's atmosphere is of short wavelength. About one-tenth of it is highly energetic ultraviolet (UV) energy, below 0.4 μm, most of which is absorbed by stratospheric oxygen and by the ozone which is created (p.7).

About a third of all the incoming radiation is returned to space by reflection from clouds and the surface, some after scattering from droplets and particles in the troposphere, while the atmosphere as a whole absorbs about one-fifth. Thus just under half reaches the surface, from which a large proportion is radiated as longwave energy, in turn absorbed by atmospheric gases, aerosols, and clouds especially by water vapour and carbon dioxide. There is back-radiation to the surface from the heated air and clouds, but a net gain to the atmosphere, as shown in I.3. Turbulence and evaporation-condensation processes also transfer energy from the surface to the lower air.

Within the global system there are regular natural energy exchanges, so that most environmental problems relate to **energy imbalance** – abnormal amounts of UV radiation; heat energy released to the air, and the uneven distribution of food and fuel energy.

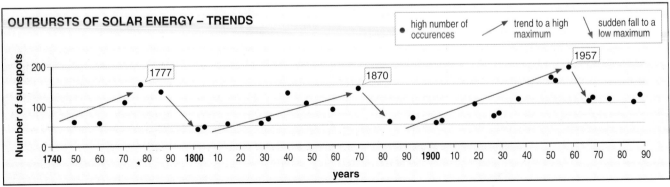

I.1 Years with exceptional outbursts of solar energy, indicated by sunspots (p.8). Notice trends in the occurrences.

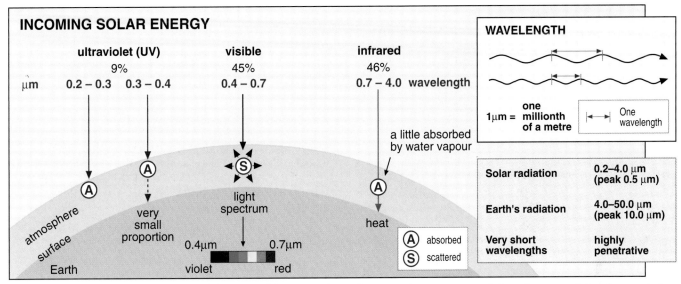

I.2 Incoming solar radiation affects the behaviour of the atmosphere, the energetic movements of air and water and the characteristics of living things, as each responds to particular wavelengths whose proportions are indicated above. The fact that the atmospheric shield selectively absorbs shortwave energy is of particular significance to the surface environment.

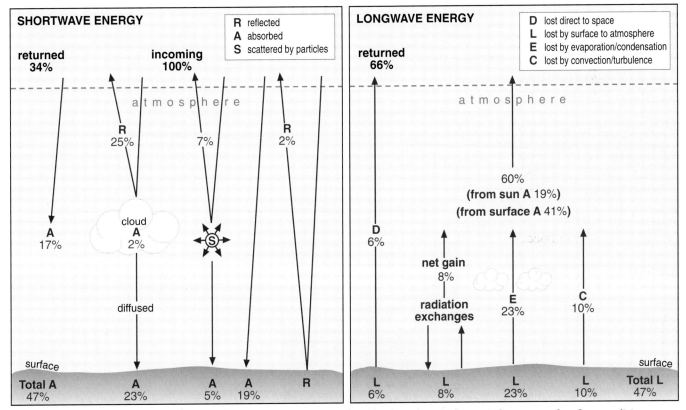

I.3 Energy exchanges, with approximate percentages on a global scale summarising the influence of a variety of surface conditions on reflection, absorption, and emission. Cloud amounts are significant. The process of condensation releases heat, and the clouds themselves reflect incoming shortwave radiation and absorb and emit longwave energy.

1

CHANGES IN THE ATMOSPHERE

- Its composition varies with altitude

- Climatic cycles over the ages

- Natural influences on climatic variation

- A 'Greenhouse Effect' – essential for lifeforms

- Carbon dioxide – its varying concentrations

- Atmospheric warming – possible consequences

- Atmospheric change – harmful or beneficial?

- Low-level pollutants: acid rain

- The 'Ozone Layer' – upper air pollution

- Atmospheric disturbance – priorities for action?

CLIMATIC CHANGE IS CONTINUOUS

Changing weather: changing climates

By definition **weather** refers to changeable atmospheric conditions. In the middle latitudes the weather can change abruptly from one moment to the next, and varies with the seasons. Near the equator there may be little seasonal variation, one day seeming much like the rest, yet during each day there are considerable variations in relative humidity, cloud cover, and vertical and horizontal air movements. In any latitude local weather conditions may be due to distant disturbances and influenced by atmospheric changes on a global scale.

Climate is seen in terms of *mean* atmospheric conditions, but these also change from one period to another. Different parts of the world have recognisable climatic characteristics with distinctive seasonal patterns, yet contrary to widespread belief, climate is not constant – **change is the norm**. Mean temperatures, humidity, precipitation, and wind direction can change considerably with time, perhaps responding to distant variations in ocean currents or changes in the surface-covering of ice or vegetation (which could be influenced by human activities).

Short-term/long-term variations

Mean seasonal conditions may vary from one decade to the next, while a hundred-year span may include long periods when climates are noticeably cooler or warmer, wetter or drier. Over longer periods there have been considerable climatic contrasts, like those in the northern hemisphere before, during, and after the 'Little Ice Age' (p.16).

Over hundreds of thousand of years global climates have swung quite abruptly from ice-age conditions to inter-glacial warmth in response to natural causes (1.4). **Some influences act cyclically**, such as the gradual regular changes in the configuration of earth's orbit, and its variations in rotation (p.8). In combination they may cause exceptional conditions to recur at fairly regular intervals. Also **the amount of energy received from the sun varies**. In the short term it emits exceptional bursts of energy, the result of internal nuclear reactions, and surface sunspots associated with such activity have shown regularities in maximun and minimum occurrences over the ages (1.6). The atmospheric composition has also varied, significantly the proportion of carbon dioxide, and we can consider how past concentrations may have influenced climatic change.

Our increasing influences

Natural influences on climatic cycles continue, but our potential for disturbance increases. Two thousand years ago there were some 400 million of us; by AD 1750 only twice as many; yet today's 5500 million could double in 50 years. Through consumerism and spreading industrialisation we release huge amounts of energy and create air pollution on an increasing scale. The atmosphere, however, is a vast complex part of our planet, and to assess our ability to change its composition and affect its behaviour we need to appreciate its characteristics.

1.1 LONG-TERM CHANGE 20 000 years ago ice filled this fertile Andean valley, plucking and wearing back the sloping spurs.

1.2 SHORT-TERM CHANGE The free-flowing Niagara Falls frozen in a matter of weeks during a severe winter.

The composition of the atmosphere

This mixture of gases and vapour, held about the planet by gravity, is extremely compressible. About half the air is within 6 km of the earth's surface and only 3 per cent is higher than 30 km. The pressure exerted by the overlying air falls rapidly with altitude (1.3).

Dry surface air is mainly nitrogen (78%) and oxygen (21%); yet small variable proportions of carbon dioxide and very small amounts of stratospheric ozone influence the surrounding air temperature and global energy distribution. The water vapour content is involved in large air-surface energy exchanges, by directly absorbing and emitting heat, and also in processes of evaporation and condensation. Absorption and emission by vegetation affect its local concentration.

Relatively small amounts of **other gases come from various natural sources**. Between them, plants, decomposing vegetation, and ruminants release methane, chloromethane, and compounds of nitrogen and sulphur, which take part in chemical reactions in the atmosphere (p.24). Some of these gases migrate slowly into the stratosphere, where they act to create a natural concentration of ozone.

Manufacturing, transport, and farming activities release these and other **gaseous pollutants** capable of raising air temperature, creating health risks and reducing the stratospheric ozone concentration.

The troposphere and stratosphere

The lower, denser atmosphere (the **troposphere**) with most of the water vapour, aerosols, and dust, is a turbulent zone where vertical and horizontal differences in air pressure and temperature make for changeable weather, and for regional variations in cloudiness and precipitation. Here the mean air temperature falls with altitude by about 6.5C° per km.

In contrast the **stratosphere** is mainly dry and dust-free. At great heights incoming UV radiation initiates photochemical processes which release heat energy. Lower down it is absorbed by the more abundant oxygen molecules and by the ozone it creates, raising the temperature considerably. This temperature inversion acts to blanket the air rising from the turbulent troposphere, forming a 'ceiling' or **tropopause** (1.3) whose height varies with latitude and with the seasons (some 16 km above the equator

but only about half that altitude over the poles). Nevertheless, gaseous pollutants can slowly enter the stratosphere, especially in the vicinity of the mid-latitude jet streams.

Ionisation at very high altitude

Above 80 km the air is very thin, only two-millionths of the atmospheric content. Here incoming X-rays and UV energy up to 0.29 µm wavelength split oxygen molecules into atoms, removing electrons and leaving positively charged ions. This zone of electrons and ions, the **ionosphere**, reflects energy at radio wavelengths, and is therefore used for communications.

The ozone 'shield'

Below the level of the ionosphere, incoming UV radiation encounters more oxygen molecules and on impact releases charged oxygen atoms. Here there is a greater possibility of these colliding with another oxygen molecule to form ozone (1.31). Some also collide with ozone and re-create oxygen molecules. Most of the UV energy is absorbed during this cycle of production and destruction.

Small amounts of natural gaseous compounds affect the concentration of high-level ozone, for instance UV energy releases ozone-destructive chlorine atoms from chloromethane. Other gases put a mild brake on this by combining with the chlorine. Such actions create the natural balance which is endangered by our additions of gaseous pollutants.

Ozone molecules drift slowly downward so that **a zone of maximum concentration** occurs between 12–35 km, varying with the latitude and season (though the actual amount of ozone is very small, some 6×10^{-5} per cent of the air by volume). At this height most of the UV energy has already been absorbed.

UV radiation can modify genetic material in living tissues so plant and animal species which have adapted to receiving amounts related to the natural ozone concentration are at risk if the UV energy reaching the surface increases. Obviously a possible depletion of the ozone 'shield' is of global concern; though the proportional depletion of stratospheric ozone varies regionally. The threats from atmospheric pollutants are dealt with in some detail on p. 24.

EARTH'S ATMOSPHERE – Vertical Zones

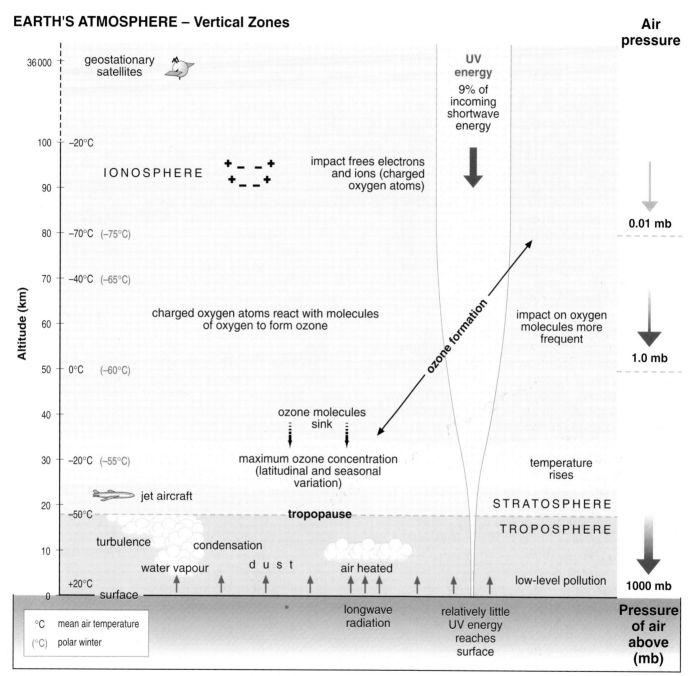

1.3 Energy exchanges create temperature anomalies which produce layering in the atmosphere. The upper boundary of the turbulent troposphere (the tropopause) tends to be higher in summer than winter. Near the Equator its altitude is some 15–16 km, whereas during winter in polar latitudes it is less than half this. Notice that in high latitudes the temperature variation with altitude changes from mid-summer to mid-winter.

- Why stress the characteristics of ultraviolet and infra-red energy when considering 'layering' of the atmosphere and turbulence in the troposphere?

- Consider why the altitude of the troposphere varies seasonally and with latitude.

- How would you argue against the widely-held view that any high-level ozone destruction means permanent depletion of the 'ozone layer'?

THE ENERGY WE RECEIVE VARIES

Cyclic variations during the earth's orbit

Even if the sun's output were constant over the millenia the energy received at a particular latitude would vary, since the angle between the earth's axis of rotation and the ecliptic plane varies by about 2.5° during a 40 000 year cycle. As the **tilt** increases, so do seasonal contrasts. Also, during a 10 500 year cycle, the spinning earth wobbles – its **axis swivels** (1.5).

Earth's orbit about the sun also varies over a 110 000 year period, from more elliptical to more circular. The more elliptical, the greater the season contrasts – earth and sun being closer in January (earth at the periphelion P) than in July (earth at aphelion A). Cyclic variation in the *position* of the ellipse (P at Px and A at Ax) also affects seasonal climates.

Such cyclic changes combine to cause variations and feedbacks in our atmospheric system, though the exact responses are not fully understood. Over long periods other factors, such as change in the concentration of carbon dioxide, may reinforce or counteract their influences. Nevertheless over 500 000 years **repeating cycles** reveal strikingly similar patterns of temperature variation (1.4) hinting at future global temperatures, but no more.

Sunspot activity

During an **exceptionally high energy outburst** magnetic disturbance creates a cool vortex on the sun's surface, seen as a sunspot. Such activity appears to reach a maximum every 11 years or so, followed by minimum activity with few sunspots. During a cycle of some 80–90 years the number of sunspots in maximum years appears to increase, then suddenly decline to a period of less activity, even in maximum years.

Such outbursts of high energy might well induce more reactions and greater warming in the stratosphere; but it is difficult to connect them with climatic changes in the troposphere, despite some remarkable coincidences between high and low sunspot occurrences and particular climatic conditions, especially the unusual lack of activity in the seventeenth century which coincided with a remarkably cold period in the northern hemisphere (1.7). On a more playful note, there is convincing evidence that in first-class cricket 'exceptional (batting) feats are produced at times of exceptional weather occuring at the extremes of the sunspot cycle'![1]

External variations do act to change climate, while human inputs may act to intensify or moderate the consequences to an extent as yet unknown.

- Global mean surface air temperature declined by some 4°C during glacial advances (at periods indicated in 1.4). Suggest where and why temperature declined much less and much more at these times.

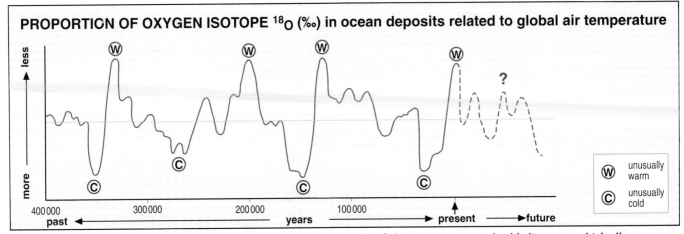

1.4 The oxygen isotope ^{18}O concentrations in ocean deposits reveal cycles of alternating warm and cold climates – which allow speculation about the future. (*After Lamb H H, based on Berger A*)[2].

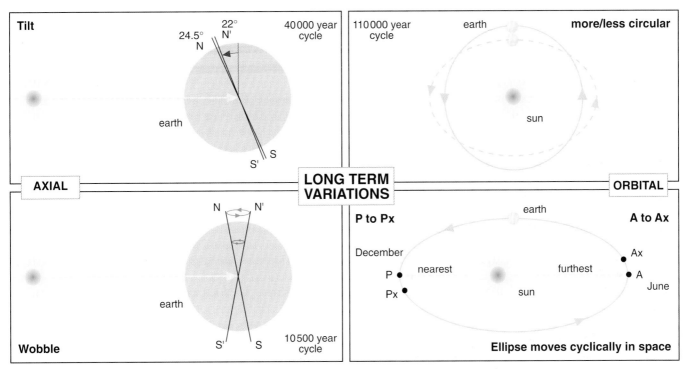

1.5 Cyclical variations which affect the amount of energy received seasonally at a particular latitude.

- Cores from deep-sea deposits and ice-caps, dated by radioactivity in contemporary debris, show that higher temperatures remove more ^{18}O from oceans and add more to ice (useful indicators of past atmospheric conditions). Suggest limitations of using fossils or ancient pollens as climatic indicators.

FLUCTUATION IN SUNSPOT NUMBERS SINCE 1880

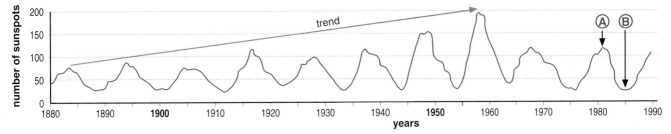

1.6 A period during which an approximate 11 year cycle has been maintained. Observations by the Solar Maximum satellite showed a 0.1 per cent decline in brightness between **A** 1980 and **B** 1985.

NUMBER OF SUNSPOTS PER DECADE 1600 - 1750 (estimated)

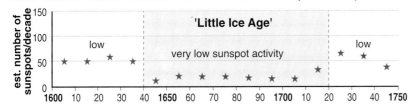

1.7 Despite this strong coincidence of minimal sunspot activity and low mid-latitude temperature in the northern hemisphere, precise relationships are not easy to establish or explain. Tropical air temperatures sometimes appear to respond directly to solar activity, sometimes inversely.

Different surfaces, different effects

Surface characteristics obviously affect the climate. The **albedo** of a surface, the proportion of the incoming shortwave energy it reflects, influences the amount absorbed and the energy emitted to heat the air above. Clean snow absorbs about a fifth of the incoming energy, whereas dirty snow absorbs more and melts more rapidly. Volcanic dust falling onto an ice surface thus causes quicker melting.

Disturbing the surface affects the local atmosphere. 1.8 shows contrasts in albedo and evaporation rates between forest and cleared land. While the latter reflects more, its directly heated surface readily passes energy to air in contact. Much of the energy received by trees boosts evapotranspiration from the leaves.

Ocean water absorbs most of the incoming energy, though currents redistribute it and evaporation cools the surface. **The oceans**, slow to warm and cool compared with land areas, **act as a great heat store**, while **currents transport huge amounts of energy** across the globe, the surface exchanging heat with the air above. Other currents slowly circulate at great depth. Air temperatures in the northern hemisphere tend to change more rapidly and to a greater extent than those in the southern 'oceanic' hemisphere (1.10), and there are more marked seasonal differences, with winds and rainfall distribution responding to temperature changes.

Changes in surface configuration

The relative positions and proportions of landmasses and oceans change with time, affecting the latitudinal air temperatures, winds, and the paths of warm and cool ocean currents. 65 millions years ago, continental climates would have responded to **different latitudinal locations** and different maritime influences (1.10). Today the removal of Arctic sea-ice would affect global climates through realignment of warm and cool currents. Some land configurations, notably the Himalayan ranges and the great Tibetan plateau, are barriers to air movements and act as climatic controls, so that **mountain building** associated with plate movements will have affected climates over the last 65 million years.

Volcanic activity – global effects

Aerosols, minute suspended particles, become concentrated in parts of the atmosphere. Volcanic eruptions can throw aerosols to heights of 5–8 km. Some may rise to 15–25 km where, with less chance of being washed down, they circulate at high altitude for several years, scattering and absorbing incoming energy.

Volcanoes also eject water vapour, carbon dioxide, and oxides of sulphur and nitrogen, which at low levels absorb longwave radiation. Nevertheless, the overall effect of large eruptions makes for global **atmospheric cooling**, temporarily opposing any greenhouse warming (p.16). This was evident for several years after the massive Krakotoa eruptions in 1883 and Mt Agung's eruptions in Bali in 1963. Sulphurous aerosols have a cooling influence, and those from Pinatubo's recent eruptions in the Philippines have been recorded at high altitudes across the globe.

As always, there are **complex feedbacks.** Water droplets forming about volcanic particles produce thick, low-level cloud which reflects much shortwave energy but may also create high cirrus layers which trap heat. Nevertheless the net effect seems to be tropospheric cooling.

Vegetation releases gases

Life-forms exchange huge amounts of **carbon dioxide** with the atmosphere, and natural fires have always contributed over the ages. Carbon from decaying vegetation is also released as **methane**, especially from swamps, which additionally generate **sulphides**, and from ricefields. The northern tundras have accumulations of decaying plant material, its decomposition checked by low winter temperatures. With higher temperatures this could release sufficient volumes of methane to boost atmospheric warming. Tropical termites and grazing ruminants, including domestic cattle, also contribute methane. Rainforest fungi act to generate **chloromethane**, some of which, with **nitrous oxide** from soil organisms and vegetation, may slowly reach the stratosphere (p.24), while the biological decay of algae and small marine plants, phytoplankton, release **sulphides** and **methyl bromide** to the atmosphere.

What is disturbing is that gases generated by human technology now match those produced by natural processes. Their effects on the atmosphere are uncertain, despite research into the likely consequences, but it is obviously wise to advocate caution.

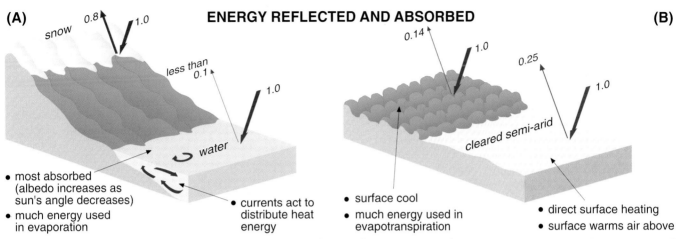

(A) snow 0.8 1.0

less than 0.1

1.0

water

ENERGY REFLECTED AND ABSORBED

(B) 0.14 1.0

0.25 1.0

cleared semi-arid

- most absorbed (albedo increases as sun's angle decreases)
- much energy used in evaporation
- currents act to distribute heat energy

- surface cool
- much energy used in evapotranspiration
- direct surface heating
- surface warms air above

1.8 The surface albedo (reflectivity) is shown as a proportion of total reflection (1.0). Surface temperature also responds to the angle of radiation impact, energy transfers (water movements in **A**), evaporation, and shading (as in **B**).

- Consider why ocean surface characteristics may be a key to world-wide climatic behaviour.

- Explain why assessment of past climatic conditions should take account of continental drift.

- Each day about 30 out of some 1500 active volcanoes emit huge volumes of gases and particles. Why is the lack of detailed information of such continuous pollution a handicap to environmentalists?

1.9 In 1991 Mount Pinatubo in the Philippines blasted out enormous masses of particles and aerosols with huge volumes of gases, including 20 million tonnes of sulphur dioxide – concentrations of which spread globally at high altitude.

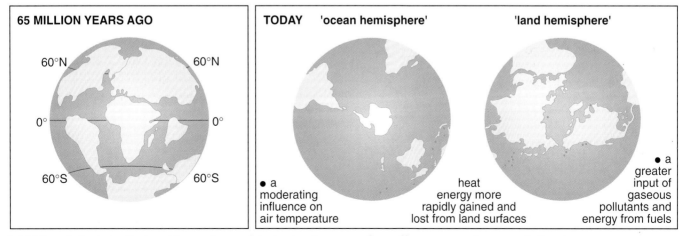

65 MILLION YEARS AGO

60°N — 60°N

0° — 0°

60°S — 60°S

TODAY   'ocean hemisphere'   'land hemisphere'

- a moderating influence on air temperature

heat energy more rapidly gained and lost from land surfaces

- a greater input of gaseous pollutants and energy from fuels

1.10 The relative latitudinal position and area of the land and ocean surfaces affect energy exchanges and climatic responses.

11

The Greenhouse Effect – essential for survival

The greenhouse analogy is used because the earth's surface, absorbing shortwave energy which has penetrated the atmosphere, radiates longwave energy and so warms the air above. The gases, vapours, and droplets, heated by absorbing surface radiation, in turn emit energy to their surroundings. The analogy is slightly flawed, for a greenhouse retains turbulent air movements, reducing energy loss.

Molecules of water vapour, in particular, absorb and re-radiate longwave energy; but so do those of carbon dioxide and the less plentiful constituents such as methane, nitrous oxide, and ozone, derived from natural and artificial sources. **This 'greenhouse effect' is essential for the survival of life-forms** adapted both to incoming shortwave radiation and energy derived from the surface.

Influences on local air temperature

Part of the longwave radiation, between 8–14 μm wavelength, is not absorbed by water vapour and the principal gases but lost to space, as through an 'atmospheric window'. However, as water droplets do absorb it, **clouds** act to 'close the window' and re-radiate heat to the air below. Cloudy nights tend to be warmer than clear ones. **Condensation** itself releases heat to surrounding air.

Local weather also varies with **imported energy and moisture**, depending on atmospheric pressure differences. Unfortunately some see an unusually warm spell as an indication of global warming rather than an indirect response to meteorological conditions, sometimes far across the globe.

Increasing concentration of 'greenhouse gases'

The relative concentrations of gases and vapours in the lower atmosphere are changing, partly through our interference with the biotic environment. Burning and clearing vegetation, extending flooded ricefields, and rearing more and more cattle increase emissions of the so-called 'greenhouse gases', while the ever-growing number of factories, dwellings and internal-combustion engines consume fossil fuels and emit gaseous wastes. Many manufactured products and by-products are released with undesirable effects.

Carbon dioxide levels have risen from an estimated pre-industrial 280 parts per million by volume to over 350 ppm, and by about a tenth in the last 30 years. Methane concentration has risen from 0.8 to 1.7 ppm, and that of nitrous oxide, emitted by power stations and cars, is rapidly increasing.

There are **feedbacks** to consider. For instance, increasing amounts of sulphur dioxide, though undesirable, may counter atmospheric warming, for its molecules reflect solar radiation and also act as nuclei for water condensation and cloud formation. The extent to which pollutants are raising global air temperature is difficult to assess or predict with any certainty. There are the external variations in energy inputs, and the fact that water vapour makes the prime contribution to atmospheric warming focuses attention on changes related to oceans, snow, ice, and vegetation.

Some of the most threatening pollutants emitted in recent years are the CFCs (chloro-fluoro-carbons), used among other things in refrigerators, electronic components, and aerosol sprays. They are present in air in small amounts, but have a great warming effect per molecule – 10 000 times that of a carbon dioxide molecule – and a long atmospheric lifetime (1.11).

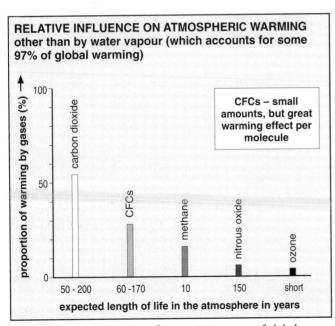

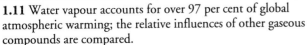

1.11 Water vapour accounts for over 97 per cent of global atmospheric warming; the relative influences of other gaseous compounds are compared.

GREENHOUSE EFFECT

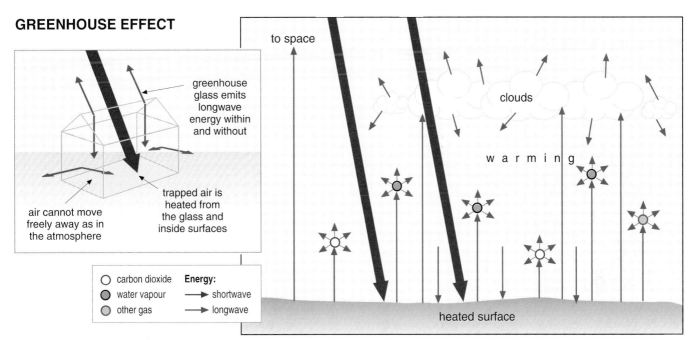

greenhouse glass emits longwave energy within and without

air cannot move freely away as in the atmosphere

trapped air is heated from the glass and inside surfaces

to space

clouds

w a r m i n g

heated surface

○ carbon dioxide
● water vapour
◐ other gas

Energy:
→ shortwave
→ longwave

1.12 Longwave energy emitted from the surface is absorbed and re-emitted by water vapour, carbon dioxide, and other gases. An extensive cloud cover, absorbing and emitting energy, helps to increase the lower air temperature.

- Issues of environmental concern overlap and may conflict. Consider why preserving wetlands, protecting buffalo herds, and seeding clouds to promote rainfall are, in theory, at odds with plans to reduce global warming.

- Discuss why increasing cloud cover may have a warming or cooling effect, and how this could vary with latitude.

- Why describe the greenhouse effect as a 'vital necessity'?

1.13 Southern China, where the buffalo, swamp, and ricefields beyond are but some of the rural elements which contribute methane to the atmosphere.

1.14 Under anticyclonic conditions in New South Wales metal works are creating visible, and invisible, air pollution, made worse by a pall from bushfires.

Organic matter and carbon cycling

Fluctuating concentrations of carbon dioxide deserve careful examination in view of its role in atmospheric warming. **The bulk of the earth's carbon occurs in the biosphere**, including oceanic life-forms, and is involved in carbon dioxide exchanges with the atmosphere. In green plants chloroplasts combine carbon dioxide and water to form carbohydrates, using only about two-thousandths of the sun's energy received. With elements from soil minerals, carbohydrates form proteins and other material for plant cells. Carbon dioxide returns to the air as living things respire and also, with methane (CH_4), as plant and animal matter decays.

Long-term storage

Plants slowly decaying under swamp conditions leave carbon concentrations in peat and in coal, compacted and preserved by overlaying mineral deposits. Much of the carbon in oceanic life-forms sinks to the ocean bed, and is eventually 'locked up' **in carbonate rocks** or in accumulations of **mineral oil** preserved within rock formations. Carbon also falls to the ocean floor as precipitated forms of carbonate. In time, naturally acidic solutions act on carbonate rocks (limestones) to release carbon dioxide, as do human activities such as lime burning.

    The oceans remove much carbon dioxide from the atmosphere. It is much more soluble in cold water than in warm, and as ice forms in polar oceans the salt increases sea-water density, so that dissolved carbon dioxide is slowly carried down to the ocean depths. Over the past century the oceans have removed about half the additional carbon dioxide; but the process is slow, so our current additions continue to increase the atmospheric concentration.

The effects of human activities

Since the industrial revolution **fossil fuel combustion** has added large quantities of carbon dioxide to the atmosphere, a proportion of which is absorbed by vegetation and ocean water. The increasing **removal of vegetation**, especially forest clearance for agriculture, affects the carbon dioxide concentration, not only by release from combustion but also by interfering with natural gaseous cycling processes, for new plant cover may not exchange or store as much carbon as before.

Responses to varying concentrations

As global climates have varied naturally through the ages, so have concentrations of atmospheric carbon dioxide. About 130 000 years ago, when mean air temperatures were slightly higher than now, its concentration was much as today – some 300 ppm. About 20 000 years ago, during the last ice advance, when mean temperatures were 4–5C° lower than today's, the carbon dioxide concentration was 190 ppm. This suggests a close relationship between the proportion of carbon dioxide in the atmosphere and the mean global surface air temperature. Yet, once again, **feedbacks question the assumption.** Whatever the causes of glacial conditions, **cooler oceans** would have dissolved a great deal of carbon dioxide and transferred huge quantities to ocean deeps over the centuries, especially in high latitude sinks, though a global **reduction in vegetation cover** would also have affected the extent of carbon dioxide exchanges between plants and the atmosphere. Converse effects in warmer inter-glacials, with higher ocean temperatures and greater concentrations of carbon dioxide, could have boosted global atmospheric warming by the greenhouse mechanism. It is tempting to attribute such warming/cooling in the past mainly to variations in carbon dioxide concentrations. They are unlikely to have been the sole cause, though they may have strongly enhanced or countered trends due to other causes.

Cutting back emissions

Assuming concentrations continue to increase at current rates, widely varying forecasts suggest a consequent rise in global surface air temperature of 0.5C° to 2.0C° by the year 2050 (1.19). However some scientists assert that above a certain concentration additional amounts would cause only a relatively small rise.

    It is generally assumed that the consequences of the increasing amounts of carbon dioxide and accompanying warming must be undesirable. Yet in some respects they may prove beneficial (p.20). Nevertheless, in view of the uncertainties, it seems prudent to cut back emissions, and it is logical to start as soon as possible. 1.16 compares the results of reducing the concentration by 2 per cent a year starting in 1995 and in 2010.

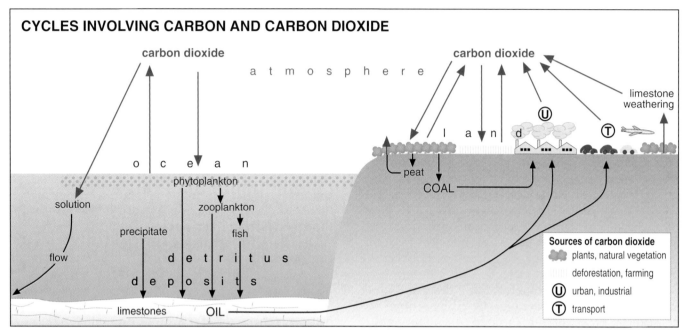

CYCLES INVOLVING CARBON AND CARBON DIOXIDE

carbon dioxide

a t m o s p h e r e

carbon dioxide

limestone weathering

l a n d

Ⓤ

Ⓣ

o c e a n

peat

COAL

phytoplankton

solution

zooplankton

precipitate

fish

flow

d e t r i t u s

d e p o s i t s

limestones   OIL

Sources of carbon dioxide
- plants, natural vegetation
- deforestation, farming
- Ⓤ urban, industrial
- Ⓣ transport

1.15 Carbon dioxide as part of a broader cycle of carbon compounds. Increasing release from fossil fuels adds to its atmospheric concentration. Oceans absorb the gas and store carbon in deep sinks, but they do so slowly.

- Burning and clearing vegetation interrupts photosynthesis, transpiration, and decay. How is carbon dioxide involved in each process?

- Carbon dioxide is said to absorb infra-red energy in only two narrow wavebands with the present concentration taking up almost all such radiation. If so, *would* additional CO_2 make for extra warming? Should this affect decisions to limit carbon dioxide emissions?

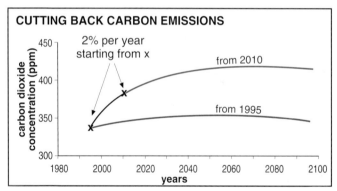

CUTTING BACK CARBON EMISSIONS

2% per year starting from x

from 2010

from 1995

carbon dioxide concentration (ppm)

450
400
350
300

1980 2000 2020 2040 2060 2080 2100

years

1.16 The advantage of early restriction of emissions.

1.17 Fires release carbon dioxide as they sweep large areas of vegetation, though they can also have beneficial effects (p.38).

1.18 As pollution from domestic coal burning in the UK decreased, emissions from power stations increased.

Evaluating the causes

In view of current gaseous emissions, the greenhouse effect is capable of creating unusual warming on a global scale. However feedbacks such as increasing cloud and unforeseen natural occurrences – variations in incoming energy, a realignment of ocean currents, or a period of volcanic activity – make it difficult to predict the extent.

It is extremely difficult to gauge how much an *observed* increase in atmospheric temperature may be due to **natural or human causes.** They may be acting together, or possibly against one another. 1.20A shows mean surface air temperatures in the northern hemisphere over the last thousand years. For most of this period we could not have affected air temperature on a global scale. There is a remarkable contrast between unusual warmth in medieval times and the subsequent fall in temperature when the northern hemisphere experienced a 'Little Ice Age'. During the particularly cold period of the seventeenth and early eighteenth centuries there were few exceptional outbursts from the sun. Yet it is as hard to account for extremely low temperatures during a prolonged sunspot minimum as to determine why frequent solar outbursts should apparently coincide with temperature increases in the lower troposphere. Nevertheless, after this period of relative inactivity cyclic increases in sunspot occurrences were accompanied by warmer conditions.

Variations during the period of industrialisation

From 1880 to 1940, a period of great industrial growth, mean surface air temperatures in the northern hemisphere rose by about 0.5C°, though the southern 'oceanic' hemisphere experienced slower warming. It is tempting to attribute warming during a period of mass-manufacturing to **increasing outputs of energy and pollutants** and the growth of urban concentrations. However **a natural recovery** to warmer conditions should also be considered, for the mid-nineteenth century was a cool period at the end of a colder one.

From 1940 into the 1970s temperatures in the northern hemisphere fell. Since then they have been variable, with a tendency to rise, and with very warm years in the late '80s and early '90s. It seems unlikely that these fluctuations have been solely due to human inputs. We may have created an underlying warming trend which has been masked by other variables, though there is no clear indication of this. NASA's satellite observations since 1979 enabled them to conclude in 1990 that these had shown no evidence of global warming.

1.21, combining land, air, and sea-surface temperatures, shows variations from the average for 1950–81, and confirms an upward trend. But, of course, **peaks and troughs** have occurred throughout. Some may be due to the cooling effect of aerosols from major volcanic eruptions (p.10); and, again, there have been fluctuations in solar emissions, though inexact correlations and uncertainty of the mechanisms which might be involved make this a controversial issue.

Possible consequences

Any warming is likely to vary regionally, with relatively small increases near the equator, considerably larger ones near the poles, and more pronounced within continental areas than over oceans. The middle latitudes could experience greater variability, with more frequent and more intense storm activity. *When* such effects might occur is still difficult to forecast. Responses are to progressive increases in pollutant levels, rather than sudden ones; also many computer inputs necessarily ignore the effects of deep oceans and interactions between atmosphere and biosphere, which diminishes confidence in their predictions.

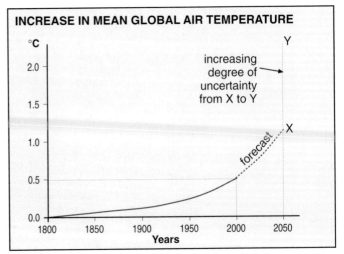

1.19 A computer forecast based on doubling the CO_2 content by 2050 while other greenhouse gases increase.

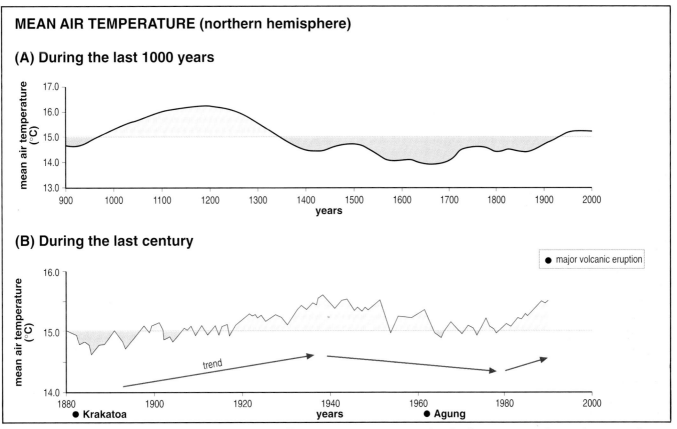

MEAN AIR TEMPERATURE (northern hemisphere)

(A) During the last 1000 years

(B) During the last century

1.20 A shows the recent recovery after several centuries of low mean temperatures, and **B** the fluctuating rise during the twentieth century. Major volcanic eruptions, two of which are shown, tend briefly to produce cooler conditions.

- Between 1880 and 1940 the winter temperature in Arctic latitudes showed an exceptional increase – over 3C° in eastern Greenland and northern Scandinavia, regions which subsequently showed the most rapid decline. Consider why.

- Scientists agree that the 0.5C° rise over a century is in the range of natural fluctuation. They admit uncertainty. But does this disprove an increasing human contribution?

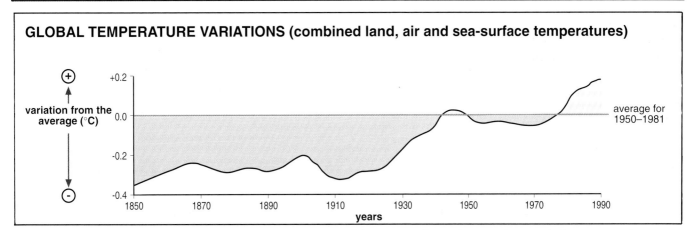

GLOBAL TEMPERATURE VARIATIONS (combined land, air and sea-surface temperatures)

1.21 A rising trend of mean global temperatures, with an increase of about 0.5C° from relative coolness in the late nineteenth century, though with a period of decline after the 1940s.

17

The Oceans – direct responses

Since the late nineteenth century **mean global sea-level** has been rising by some 1–2 mm a year, due mainly to thermal expansion and the receipt of ice-melt water. The response to any atmospheric warming tends to be delayed, however, a current increase in global air temperature would make for further sea-level rise well into the twenty-first century.

During the early 1980s there were predictions for a rise of some eight metres by 2050, but recent estimates suggest an increase of 30 cm, or perhaps less. **Thermal expansion** would account for about half of this, though, as with air temperatures, the amplitude would vary from region to region.

Sea-level is also likely to rise as more **glacial meltwater** flows in. It is difficult to evaluate the extent of this contribution, for the rate of melting would vary with the latitude and altitude of glaciers and ice-sheets. Contributions from the Greenland and Antarctic ice-sheets are expected to be relatively small, as discussed below. Melting sea-ice would have little effect, for as it floats it displaces its own weight of water.

Other factors make it difficult to predict **future sea-levels and possible effects on coastlands.** A large increase in ocean water might lead to some compensatory sinking of the ocean floor. In general, sediment-laden deltas make for subsidence, though some deltaic lowlands which appear to be under threat are subject to tectonic movements with occasional uplift, as in southern Bangladesh. Excessive oil and water extraction causes subsidence and can make some coastlands vulnerable, particularly that about Los Angeles (p.35). As suggested above, any sea-level rise is likely to be slow and may be contained by sea defences. But even small rises add to the danger from surges caused by atmospheric disturbances.

Global warming – oceanic feedback

As oceans comprise 70 per cent of the global surface their response to atmospheric warming could produce climatically important, though uncertain, feedbacks. Surface warming is likely to increase the atmospheric water vapour and carbon dioxide contents (1.22) making for higher 'greenhouse-induced' temperatures. But though extra condensation would release more energy to the atmosphere, denser cloud in the lower and middle levels would reflect more incoming radiation. Then again, more high-level cirrus clouds

might well trap longwave radiation and have a warming effect. **The influence of clouds** on possible greenhouse warming is one of the main imponderables.

Ice-sheets and glaciers

The likelihood of total loss of the polar ice-caps has been luridly treated by sections of the press. It would need exceptionally high temperatures to remove all **Antarctic ice**, which has a mean thickness of 2.5 km over an area the size of the USA. More justifiable are fears that low-level melting might induce surges of ice into the ocean or that the West Antarctic sheet might break up, for this rests partly on a bed below the sea and detachment might cause a sea-level rise of several metres, though at the moment this seems unlikely.

As 1.24 indicates, Antarctica receives a moist summer inflow. As additional snow, which reflects incoming energy, accumulates on the cold surface the high-level ice should gradually increase in volume, and satellite evidence indicates that in recent years this has been happening over much of Antarctica.

In other parts of the world, for much the same reason, the sources of high-level glaciers have received additional snow during warmer periods, causing glacial advances. However, rising temperatures have caused the retreat of low glaciers and melting of fringe-ice and sea-ice. A considerable disappearance of sea-ice would not directly create a rise in sea-level, but might allow surface currents to import energy into polar regions, causing a more general loss of ice and climatic disturbance.

Overall, any continued global atmospheric warming with ocean expansion and inputs of melt-water should increase sea-levels, though this would occur slowly. The effects on coastal areas, however, would depend on local physical and economic circumstances (p.34).

- When considering a possible rise in sea-level, why is it important to distinguish between factors making for a general increase in the volume of ocean waters and those likely to cause variation in level at a specific locality?

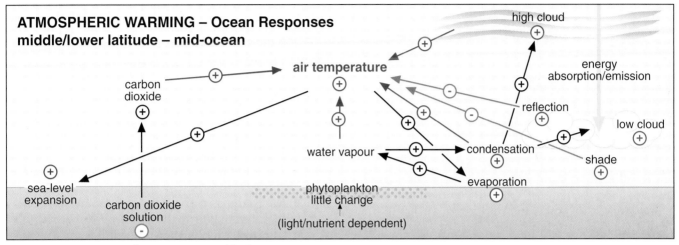

1.22 Responses to atmospheric warming and higher sea-surface temperature, with feedbacks which could make for further warming.

● The oceans' mean annual receipt of 1260 mm (precipitation and run-off) is countered by evaporation. Are estimates of sea-level rise based purely on thermal expansion and melt-water inputs likely to be accurate?

1.23 New Zealand's Franz Josef glacier has retreated from this wooded moraine (M-M) to a snout 230 m higher up.

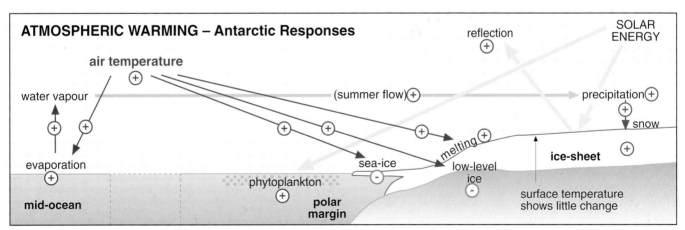

1.24 Moist air moving into high Antarctica may gradually increase the ice volume, whereas low-level ice may melt more rapidly. Page 30 considers the effect of atmospheric exchanges with the abundant phytoplankton.

Predicted changes – uncertain consequences

Crop distribution and yields depend on numerous interactions and feedbacks between climatic components, such as energy intensity, air temperature, water availability, and carbon dioxide concentration. With sufficient sunshine a higher temperature may induce faster growth but will increase evapotranspiration, so that moisture loss means a shorter growing-season; and while changes in rainfall amount and seasonal distribution would affect yields, much would depend on soil conditions. In 1.25 predicted changes in rainfall and temperature should be considered *together* when assessing possible harm or benefit, and, of course, these estimates are subject to a high uncertainty range.

Carbon dioxide and crop yields

Its contribution to global warming casts carbon dioxide as a major villain, even though **a higher concentration may benefit plants** by stimulating photosynthesis, promoting growth and expanding the leaf area. Its increasing concentration tends progressively to close leaf stomata, reducing water loss through transpiration. The plant's water requirements are less, so water-use efficiency is greater; and as the shade of denser leaf canopy reduces moisture loss, irrigation is more effective.

Under *experimental* conditions, doubling carbon dioxide concentration has **increased yields of food crops** by varying amounts – wheat, barley, rice, and soy beans by 10–50 per cent, those of maize, sorghum and sugar cane up to 10 per cent. This is an important consideration for less developed countries. However, as some plants release more carbohydrates they experience *nutrient deficiency*, for an increasing biomass of bacteria and fungi denies them nitrogen.

Predictions and uncertainties

In **central North America** higher mean temperatures, decreasing the effectiveness of summer rain, could adversely affect yields, especially in the southern parts of the Wheat Belt. However, the main growing areas may be extended northward and more suitable crop varieties introduced. Changes would be slow and erratic, and unlikely to devastate these great granaries, despite doom-laden assertions. Climatic change in the more technically developed countries should be less of a problem than elsewhere.

In the densely populated **southern Asian Monsoon lands** changing climatic conditions affect soil structures and crop yields of **those with less ability to adjust.** Predictions summarised in 1.25 suggest an overall benefit from increasing summer rainfall, offset by higher temperatures and greater evaporation, which would particularly affect the millions who farm the marginal lands.

The strength and reliability of the Indian monsoon varies from year to year (p.32), but higher temperatures and a stronger monsoon may also strengthen the flow of the upper easterlies, vigorous winds generated high in the troposphere (1.26). These cross Africa south of the Sahara as an easterly jet stream, whose strengthening and weakening are partial controls over the incidence of summer storms and rainfall in **the dry Sahel lands.** There the estimated changes by 2030 indicate both warming and increased rainfall; so here, too, the net result could be drier soil conditions, though there will continue to be great annual variations between different parts of the Sahel. Moreover, the models used for such predictions do not take the wider global influences into account (p.32).

These are but three areas for which climatic changes are predicted – with low confidence. Regular shifts of climatic regions are unlikely to accompany any global warming, and certainly **it would not mean drier conditions everywhere.** Moist air drawn into continental areas by stronger convection may well make dry marginal lands moister. Elsewhere there could be more frequent extremes – floods, droughts, frosts – with harmful consequences.

- By itself, mean air temperature tells little of conditions suitable for crops. Significant influences include temperature at seed depth, the photo-period (energy received by daylight), and frost risks. Consider the limitations of using statistical forecasts (1.25) to predict benefits or disasters.

CHANGES BY THE YEAR 2030 (estimated)

	area of changes	⬅ easterly jet stream

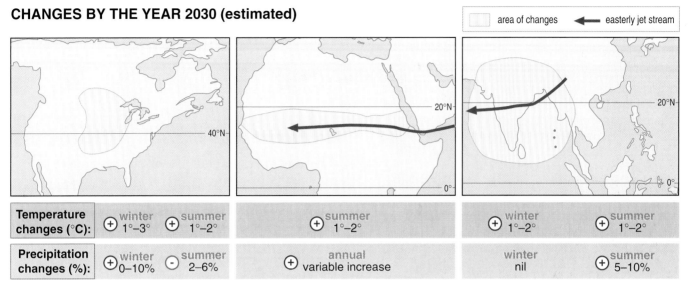

Temperature changes (°C):	⊕ winter 1°–3°	⊕ summer 1°–2°	⊕ summer 1°–2°	⊕ winter 1°–2°	⊕ summer 1°–2°
Precipitation changes (%):	⊕ winter 0–10%	⊖ summer 2–6%	⊕ annual variable increase	winter nil	⊕ summer 5–10%

1.25 Predictions of possible climatic changes for three continental areas.

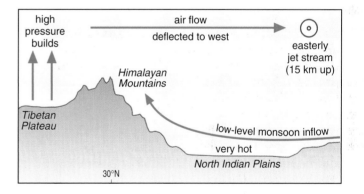

1.26 *(right)* During mid-summer air moving in response to high pressure created above the Tibetan Plateau is deflected to form an easterly jet stream, which can affect climatic conditions from India to West Africa.

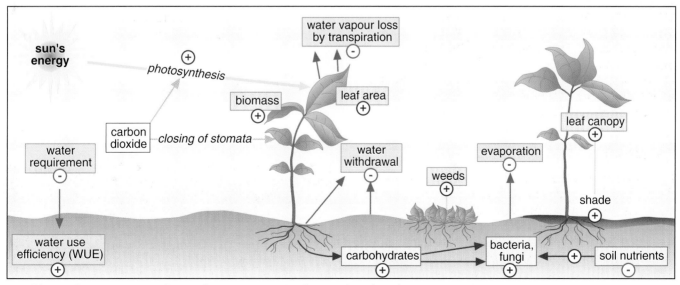

1.27 Plant-soil responses to a substantial increase in atmospheric carbon dioxide.

21

THE DISTRIBUTION OF ATMOSPHERIC POLLUTANTS

Contaminating the lower atmosphere

In the early stages of industrial development factories belched out smoke and chemical pollutants indiscriminately, and domestic coalfires polluted urban areas (p.15). In Britain dense, particle-laden urban fog (smog) would persist for days under anticyclonic conditions, a dangerous health hazard which declined after **the Clean Air Act of 1956** created smoke-free zones.

Nevertheless, power stations and factories, many using sulphur-rich fuels, continue to emit mixtures of particles, aerosols, and chemical fumes, including sulphur compounds and nitrogen oxides. Those subsiding close to the source of emission, as so-called **'dry deposition'**, lead to corrosion and health problems. 1.29 illustrates the devastation which can occur in the vicinity of metal works emitting high concentrations of acidic gases. When such fumes rise higher and drift downwind, oxidation and solution transform them into fine acidic aerosols, which may travel hundreds of kilometres before falling as **'wet deposits'** – acid rain.

Acid rain – biological effects

Downwind of a large industrial complex acid precipitation, contaminated rain or snowflakes, may **increase soil acidity** to a level at which the aluminium present forms a soluble sulphate which damages plant root-cells, and allows harmful viruses to invade trees. In parts of Scandinavia and Bavaria, downwind of major European industrial areas, numerous conifers have suffered root damage and consequent loss of needles; though top-thinning of Bavarian spruce has also been attributed to too-rapid growth – acid rain acting as a fertiliser!

The effects vary with rocks and soils. Basic soils, developed on limestones for example, act to neutralise acidity. But thin soils developed on well-watered granites are naturally acidic and run-off from such soils together with acid precipitation can make lakes incapable of supporting fish species intolerant of such acidity. Other species, and some insects and water plants, may tolerate more acidic conditions – but the biotic associations must change. In Scandinavia lake acidification is due both to imported pollutants and continual cropping of large areas of replanted conifers, which increases soil acidity and allows greater run-off.

It is essential to restrict such gaseous emissions. There has been increasing lake acidity in granitic areas of Scotland. But surveys have failed to reveal any general pattern of forest decline in Britain, and point out that trees in fine condition occur in the most polluted areas.[3]

Emissions from vehicles and from consumer products

The ever-increasing number of cars emit huge volumes of nitrogen oxides, carbon monoxide, and hydrocarbons. Incoming UV energy converts them to a mixture of ozone, aldehydes, and peroxyacetyl nitrates (PAN) – an irritant, poisonous collection which, in urban areas, blanketed by sinking air, remains concentrated as **photochemical smog**; thus in summer such conditions are notoriously dangerous to health in cities like Athens and Los Angeles.

Besides emissions of lead, cadmium, and other metal compounds from vehicles and factories, new technologies have created long-lasting pollutants such as the **CFCs (chloro-fluoro-carbons)**, widely used for aerosol propellants and in refrigerators. They make for atmospheric heating, have a long, stable life and gradually infiltrate the stratosphere (p.24). Industrially developed countries have agreed to timed bans on CFC emissions – but there are problems in imposing universal restrictions (p.82).

There are also dangers of accidental pollution from nuclear power stations, even when carefully located in relation to active fault lines or population clusters. As at Chernobyl, the effects could be horrific locally and also further afield. Nuclear waste disposal is a further problem (p.64).

Agricultural practices add significantly to low-level pollution (p.54), and methyl bromide, used to sterilise soils, also threatens stratospheric ozone.

- Suggest why there is so much variation in lake acidification in Britain, and why some catchment areas are particularly susceptible to acid deposition while others are not.

- Explain why assessing the condition of British trees means considering the spate of landscaping and field enclosure in the late eighteenth and early nineteenth centuries.

CFCs: 10000 times the molecular warming effect of carbon dioxide

very stable

long life (over 100 years)

drift to high levels as aerosols

slowly spread world-wide

concentrate in favourable circumstances (as in Antarctic ice-clouds)

UV energy breaks up their molecules – releasing ozone destructive, renewable chlorine

1.28 Reasons for an effective ban on CFC production and use.

- Tall factory chimneys and power stations are considered a mixed blessing. Consider weather conditions which would emphasise this.

- Why is it now necessary for the BBC to broadcast health warnings during summer anticyclonic conditions?

1.29 (*right*) The devastating effect of sulphurous fumes on forest and landforms downwind of copper smelting at Queenstown, Tasmania.

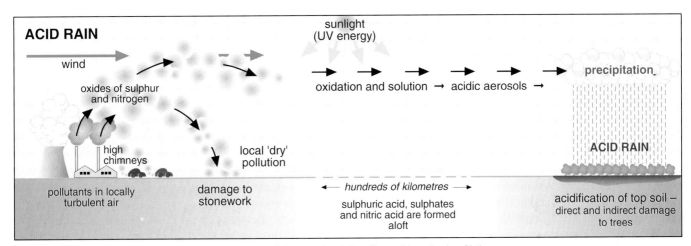

ACID RAIN

sunlight (UV energy)

wind

oxides of sulphur and nitrogen

high chimneys

local 'dry' pollution

oxidation and solution → acidic aerosols →

precipitation

ACID RAIN

pollutants in locally turbulent air

damage to stonework

← *hundreds of kilometres* →

sulphuric acid, sulphates and nitric acid are formed aloft

acidification of top soil – direct and indirect damage to trees

1.30 Releasing acidic oxides can cause environmental damage both locally and hundreds of kilometres away.

THE 'OZONE LAYER' — DISTURBING THE BALANCE

Ozone creation in the stratosphere

Some 80 km above the earth's surface, incoming UV energy encounters sufficient scattered oxygen molecules to create ozone. Each molecule splits into energetic atoms, some of which combine with another oxygen molecule to form ozone, releasing heat energy. An ozone molecule itself may be fragmented by UV energy, releasing an oxygen molecule and an atom (1.31). Such processes absorb a proportion of the incoming energy. Lower in the stratosphere, where such encounters are more numerous, the ozone concentration increases and the temperature rises. About 40 km up, the rates of creation and destruction are roughly balanced. **At 35 km most of the UV energy has been absorbed**, while a downward drift causes a maximum ozone concentration between 12–35 km.

A small proportion of the nitrogen oxides and chloromethane released from decaying vegetation and forest fires slowly enters the stratosphere. The former destroy ozone in a cycle of reactions, and the chloromethane releases ozone-destructive chlorine (1.31). These and other **chemicals from biogenic sources** have long affected **the dynamic equilibrium of stratospheric ozone** and regulated the mean amounts of UV energy reaching the surface. On earth plant and animal species have developed characteristics which enable them to flourish in this intensity of shortwave radiation.

Artificial pollutants threaten the balance

Today, bent on 'improving living standards', we manufacture potentially dangerous pollutants and release gases capable of entering and remaining in the stratosphere. They include nitrogen oxides, methyl bromide, and the long-lived CFCs, all of which endanger the ozone equilibrium. Chlorine from CFCs and chloromethane destroy ozone, while the chlorine oxide produced can react with a free oxygen atom to liberate chlorine again. There is a moderate braking mechanism, for nitrogen dioxide reacts with chlorine oxide to form stable chlorine nitrate, and in time other reactions remove chlorine from the cycle. Meanwhile **the ozone concentration is significantly reduced**, allowing more intense UV energy to affect living tissues.

Antarctica — the special case

Ozone concentration varies with latitude and season. In low latitudes receiving intense ozone-creating energy through the year, the maximum concentration is about 35 km up, a proportion of which is slowly transported polewards. **In the Antarctic** where the main concentration is at 15–20 km, ozone production ceases during the polar winter. Early in spring the concentration falls abruptly, but is then regenerated during summer when ozone is formed during unbroken periods of incoming solar energy reinforced by a slow stratospheric drift from the tropics.

In winter, with low temperature at high altitudes, strong winds encircle a vortex in the stratosphere, into which natural and artificial pollutants sink. It is so cold that stratospheric ice clouds form. These absorb nitrogen dioxide but convert it to nitric acid, so unfortunately it is not available in the spring to remove chlorine atoms. Also in winter chlorine from CFCs is held in crystals as hydrogen chloride. In spring this reacts with nitric acid to produce chlorine molecules.

During spring, therefore, as solar energy frees chlorine atoms, a rapid loss of ozone occurs, falling by 40 per cent or more and **forming the so-called 'hole'** over parts of Antarctica. As the vortex breaks down, surges of ozone-depleted air move outward. Several weeks later **the hole is mended by ozone creation**, and with importations from lower latitudes, the concentration increases again until late summer.

Exceptional ozone depletion can delay spring warming in the stratosphere and the breakdown of the vortex, a feedback which accentuates ozone destruction. **Progressively greater depletion** has occurred over several decades, especially during the early 1980s, though in some years losses have been less severe. Unusual amounts of **pollutants of volcanic origin** complicate the issue. Mt Erebus has contaminated both atmosphere and ice over a wide area, and some see the sharp depletion in 1992 and 1993 as related to Pinatubo's eruptions.

The northern polar vortex receives many pollutants, but is less stable. High-level inflows, with sinking, occur during winter so the system breaks down irregularly. In temperate latitudes the stratospheric ozone concentration is apt to fluctuate but overall the stability and long life of CFCs already released must make for further ozone loss in the long term.

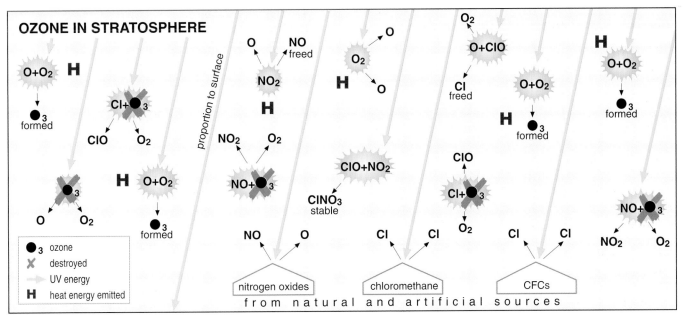

1.31 High-level ozone is created and destroyed by reactions with molecules from natural and artificial sources. Energy released and absorbed warms the stratosphere. Notice how destructive chlorine and nitric oxide may be re-released.

- Consider why the stratospheric ozone concentration at any latitude may fluctuate, and why we should examine more long-term trends.

- Why do winter air temperatures over Antarctica continue to fall to such an altitude, and why are the effects of chemical pollutants unique to this part of the globe?

- Explain why the catch-phrases 'destruction of the ozone layer' and 'hole in the ozone layer' are misleading over-simplifications.

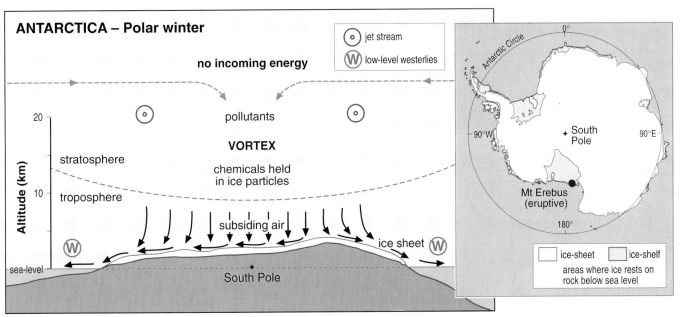

1.32 Unique atmospheric winter conditions which make for springtime destruction of high-level ozone.

ATMOSPHERIC DISTURBANCE — PRIORITIES FOR ACTION

When assessing the environmental threats which atmospheric disturbance may trigger, the likely consequences, and the extent of human involvement, if any, we should also weigh up the degree of certainty of such things happening. We can then consider priorities for suitable preventive action, keeping an eye on possible feedbacks as a result of such action. Among the issues to consider are the following.

Global warming

- A 0.5C° increase in mean surface air temperature over a century is in the range of natural fluctuation – a recovery from cooler conditions?
- Over the centuries warm and cold conditions have alternated irregularly in response to natural variables.
- The current volume of atmospheric pollutants is theoretically capable of raising air temperature at a faster rate than ever before.
- Climatic change could affect agricultural practices, with poorer communities in marginal lands most at risk.
- Global air temperature increase need not be universally disastrous: feedbacks may create more acceptable conditions in some regions.
- Increasing carbon dioxide concentration may have certain beneficial effects.
- Global warming is accompanied by rising sea-level, as yet relatively slowly.
- Computer-generated predictions of future temperature increases are unlikely to be absolutely acceptable, with insufficient inputs related to such influential variables as ocean behaviour or cloud formation.

What should our priorities be? Is it worth taking risks? Will huge investments to control various emissions enable us to prevent climatic change? Would it be better to try to control other forms of pollution? Ought we to concentrate on other environmental problems? Need there be a choice?

Threats to stratospheric ozone

- The consequences of CFC pollution are so well established that steps to ban their use in manufacturing are already being taken.
- Helping less developed countries purchase or produce alternative 'safe' products should be a priority.

- There appears to be progressive depletion of spring/summer ozone concentration over Antarctica. The extent of any loss in middle latitudes is less easy to establish.
- The conception that stratospheric ozone concentration once reduced cannot be re-established is erroneous. Nevertheless, with so many long-lasting pollutants, a slow widespread depletion seems likely.
- To what extent should one emphasise the possible dangers of ozone depletion?
  Increasing incidence of skin cancers may have other causes: more foreign travel; more sun-seeking by more people; the 'Benidorm effect'.
- The ability of lifeforms to adapt to more intensive UV radiation varies.
  With such uncertainties, it seems wise to take every possible precaution to prevent the emission of potentially ozone-destructive chemicals, while avoiding unnecessary panic.

Pollution in the lower atmosphere

- Emissions from vehicle exhausts are health hazards. Technological improvements to engines and fuels, limiting usage, and control through taxation are all feasible.
- Some pollutant controls may be linked with environmentally helpful actions, making use of methane from waste dumps, for example.
- Legislation and investment to absorb sulphurous emissions from factories and power stations seem justifiable. The emissions are noxious and create acid rain, though to a small extent they may act to offset global warming.
- Pollution from rural practices can be controlled in developed countries. It is less easy to insist on reforms in poorer, over-populated, under-funded countries where 'normal' agricultural practices may pollute the atmosphere.

Here we seek priorites for controlling atmospheric disturbance – urgent, less urgent, or perhaps hardly needed at all. Examining hazards affecting the world's oceans, vegetation, and animal life will stress that their problems are often inter-linked, which adds to the difficulties of establishing where our main priorities for actions should lie.

ATMOSPHERIC POLLUTANTS
(% from each source)

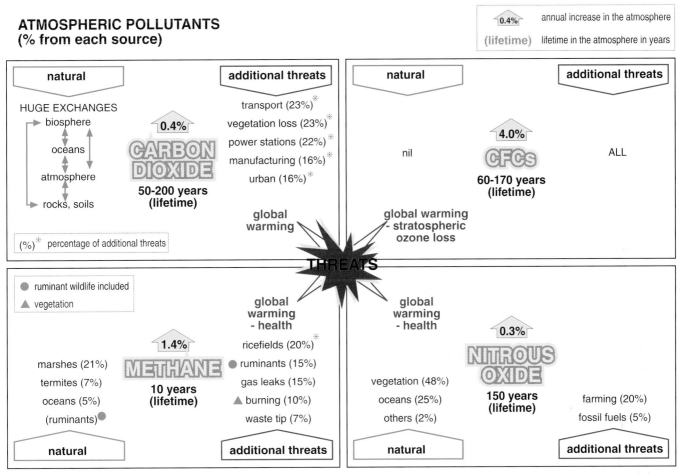

0.4% annual increase in the atmosphere

(lifetime) lifetime in the atmosphere in years

natural | **additional threats**

HUGE EXCHANGES
- biosphere
- oceans
- atmosphere
- rocks, soils

0.4%

CARBON DIOXIDE

50-200 years (lifetime)

transport (23%)*
vegetation loss (23%)*
power stations (22%)*
manufacturing (16%)*
urban (16%)*

(%)* percentage of additional threats

global warming

natural | **additional threats**

nil

4.0%

CFCs

60-170 years (lifetime)

ALL

global warming
- stratospheric ozone loss

THREATS

● ruminant wildlife included
▲ vegetation

global warming
- health

1.4%

METHANE

10 years (lifetime)

marshes (21%)
termites (7%)
oceans (5%)
(ruminants)●

ricefields (20%)*
● ruminants (15%)
gas leaks (15%)
▲ burning (10%)
waste tip (7%)

natural | **additional threats**

global warming
- health

0.3%

NITROUS OXIDE

150 years (lifetime)

vegetation (48%)
oceans (25%)
others (2%)

farming (20%)
fossil fuels (5%)

natural | **additional threats**

1.33 The proportion of atmospheric gases and aerosols contributed by natural sources and artificial release; their durability, and the threats they pose.

- Which forms of atmospheric disturbance appear likely to have the most severe environmental repercussions?

- Consider priorities for funding methods to counter potentially harmful atmospheric disturbance. Discuss the feasibility of universal remedies in view of contrasting social and economic conditions across the globe.

1.34 Under sinking air, factory emissions and dust blanket Lima's industrial suburbs. Demands of the rapidly increasing population have reduced the river Rimac to a trickle.

2

CHANGES IN THE OCEAN

- Reservoirs essential to global life

- Energy gained, held, transmitted

- Disturbing ocean food chains

- Responses to direct pollution

- The oceans and global climates

- Rising sea-level: possible consequences

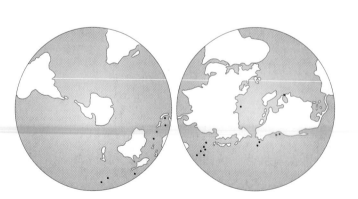

Nearly three-quarters of the earth's surface is water.

Vast area, great depth, huge volume

Almost three-quarters of the global surface is ocean water, an enormous volume with an average depth of 2800 metres, its density controlled by temperature and salinity. Very cold water sinks to great depths, where it circulates sluggishly for a long time. Evaporation cools surface water, increasing salinity and inducing it to sink. There are, however, considerable differences in temperature, density, salinity, clarity, and nutrient content between surface water in open oceans, over continental shelves, in estuaries, about coral reefs, and where water upwells. There are also differences in its ability to support marine life – its **productivity.**

The ocean's chemical content has changed little for 200 million years, with relative proportions of sodium, chlorine, magnesium, and calcium almost constant. In the top 100 metres or so, bicarbonates, phosphates, nitrates, and sulphates are extracted by primary marine plants – tiny **phytoplankton**. The word plankton ('wanderer' – *Gk.*) reflects their ability to move on after depleting the surrounding water of nutrients. Vast numbers of minute marine animals, **zooplankton**, graze them. Their energy passes to fish which abound in plankton-rich seas.

The intensity and wavelength of light energy affect the rate of growth and distribution of plankton (2.1) – little penetrates below 100 metres. In low latitudes, **photosynthetic activity** is greatest some 20 metres down, but nearer the surface in sub-polar oceans. Phytoplankton are best suited to relatively cool water.

Salts of sodium, magnesium and zinc are extracted commercially on a large scale, but to obtain many of the metals present in solution would require huge energy inputs. On the ocean beds are potentially valuable nodules of manganese (deep) and phosphorite (on shelves).

Storage and circulation of energy

Most incoming energy falls on the ocean – **a great energy reservoir**, slowly gaining and losing heat. Upper-water temperature varies seasonally down to some 400 metres. As winds impels surface water, **regular currents transfer huge amounts of energy**, directed by land barriers and the earth's rotation. Surface waters affect air temperature, both directly and through energy exchanges during evaporation and subsequent cloud formation, and maritime air influences the climates of adjoining landmasses and their potential water supplies.

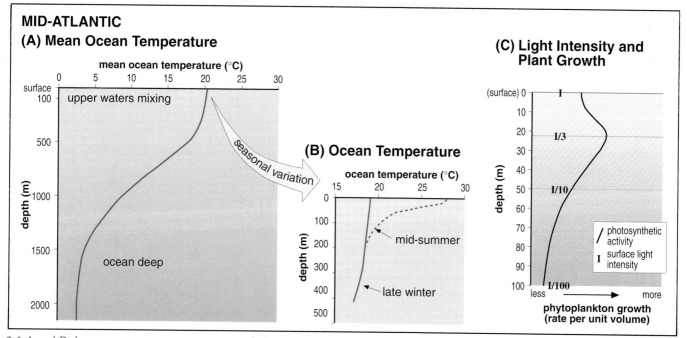

2.1 A and **B** show ocean temperature varying with depth and with season in response to solar inputs, though modified by currents (2.3). **C** shows light intensity variation in tropical waters and the depth which best suits phytoplankton development.

DISTURBING THE OCEAN FOOD CHAINS

Productive and less productive waters

Primary marine production depends greatly on concentration of nutrients, especially compounds of nitrogen and phosphorus. Large quantities of phosphates are derived from the land. In low latitudes intense light inhibits plankton development and overlying warm water acts against upward movements of nutrients, so that mid-ocean areas between 30°N and 30°S are not very productive. By contrast, waters over **continental shelves**, with nutrients from river estuaries, **have high productivity**, though the important spring outflow of nutrients may be checked where dams retain water for summer release.

Nutrient-rich upwelling waters encourage plankton growth, notably off the coasts of Peru and south-west Africa. There, winds, move cool surface waters away from the land, bringing nitrates, phosphates and other nutrients to the top 100 metres (2.4). To a lesser degree productivity increases where water diverges either side of the Equatorial Counter-Current. There is great spring productivity where cold water upwells off Antarctica (2.3). **Abundant phytoplankton** feed vast numbers of small crustacea (**krill**) which support numerous fish and birds in a food chain (simplified in 2.3). The cold waters have fewer marine species than the tropics, where life-cycles are rapid, but greater total abundance.

Exchanges with the atmosphere

As oceans and their plant life absorb much carbon dioxide, and as carbon in detritus and organic wastes sinks to the depths, to some extent they counter its increasing atmospheric concentration, though rates of removal are slow. Plankton release oxygen and denitrifying bacteria return nitrogen to the air via solution. Phytoplankton also emit dimethyl sulphide (DMS), which is oxidised to sulphate and released by spray in tiny droplets. These act as nuclei for condensation, making for considerable **cloud formation** which, reflecting incoming radiation, may both influence plankton productivity and counter global warming – feedbacks which are difficult to quantify. Some plankton species appear vulnerable to more intense radiation due to stratospheric ozone depletion; but the relatively shallow UV penetration, the depth at which plankton multiply (2.1), and the ability of lifeforms to adapt should be taken into account.

Pollution and the food chains

Marine life in shallow waters over continental shelves receives urban and industrial wastes, noxious substances which become concentrated as they pass up the food chain (2.2). Pollutants are dispersed through inter-connecting oceans. Globally, plankton are prime recipients, so that, for example, DDT (now banned) built up in Antarctic penguins. In 50 years motor fuels increased Pacific lead concentration ten-fold.

Oil spillages drastically affect local marine life, though crude oil, being organic, breaks down quickly. Even in the Baltic and Persian Gulf, with their relatively poor circulation, the effects of massive oil pollution have proved short-lived. Oil spills, despite widespread publicity, may prove less damaging environmentally than **emissions of mercury**, which restrict fishing in several parts of the world. However, oil film spreads so widely that it may affect ocean reflectivity and hence the atmosphere.

Over-fishing

Agreed restrictions on fishing are now essential to replenish stocks. In Peruvian coastal waters (2.4), plundering anchovy for fishmeal caused the loss of millions of sea birds, as did the exceptional Warm Event of 1983. At the lower end of the chain, harvesting krill on a large scale for foodstuff and animal feed could affect populations of whales, seals, fishes, penguins, and other sea birds. Even though annual Antarctic krill production is an enormous 1800 million tonnes, scientific management is called for.

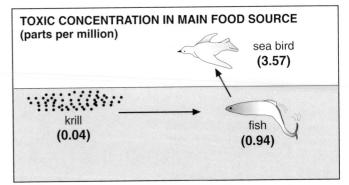

TOXIC CONCENTRATION IN MAIN FOOD SOURCE (parts per million)

sea bird **(3.57)**

krill **(0.04)**

fish **(0.94)**

2.2 Concentrations of toxic substances build up in predators consuming large quantities of polluted organisms lower in the food chain.

(A) ATLANTIC OCEAN

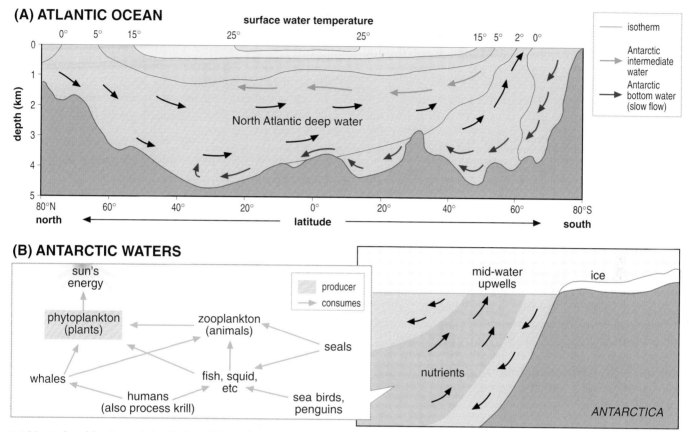

2.3 Vertical and horizontal circulations (**A**) combine to concentrate nutrients in near-surface waters, where they support chains of abundant life-forms (**B**).

- Consider why fish populations with characteristic food chains are concentrated in relatively small zones within the vast oceans. Identify those particularly vulnerable to industrial effluents, oil spillage, depletion by selective fishing, or effects of climatic variability (see p.32).

- 'Threats to phytoplankton development are of prime environmental concern'. Why does this particularly apply to those in high latitudes?

PERU CURRENT

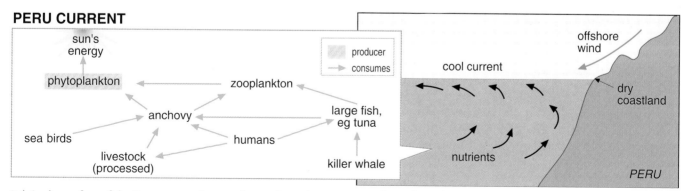

2.4 As the surface of the Peru current is moved away from the coast, upwelling allows favourably cool, nutrient-rich water to support productive food chains.

THE OCEANS AND CLIMATIC VARIABILITY

The extent to which we can influence climatic conditions and weather phenomena worldwide and make for greater variability is debatable. It is tempting to attribute such disasters as hurricanes, floods, or droughts to our interference with 'normal' atmospheric conditions, but such disasters have occurred over the ages, in some places with surprising regularity. Here we look at the inter-dependence of atmospheric circulations and find that we *could* trigger changes throughout these vast systems.

Energy from the oceans

As the surface supplies so much energy to the air, it is not surprising that the extensive oceans have a controlling influence over global climatic systems, or that **variations in sea-surface temperatures** can affect weather conditions far across the globe. In the tropics convectional uplift over heated land areas, fed by moisture from the oceans, releases enormous amounts of energy high in the troposphere (2.6). In the summer monsoons of south-east Asia ocean surfaces transfer energy to inflowing moist air and may thus stimulate upper-air circulations (2.5).

Natural circulations – periodic disasters

Tremendous exchanges of air occur in low latitudes over the Pacific Ocean in the circulation known as **The Walker Cell** (2.5). Strong convective uprisings during the Asiatic monsoons and in the western Pacific feed an eastward flow in the upper troposphere, with subsidence over the eastern Pacific. The circulation is particularly strong when Indian Ocean surface temperatures are high. From the eastern Pacific low-level air normally returns westward as the Trade Winds, moving surface water away from the coast so that the cold Peru current receives up-welling nutrients (2.4). **Every few years**, however, with weaker monsoonal activity in south-east Asia, the Walker circulation is disturbed. Warm water surges eastward across the Pacific as a **'Warm Event'**, usually about Christmas time (an **'El Niño'** or 'Christ Child' event), though not always. A surface layer of warm water prevents upwelling, with a loss of plankton and a disappearance of anchovy. With upper air subsidence weakened, storms develop and torrential rains cause landslides and floods on the normally arid coastland. At such times pressure tends to be high over eastern Australia, leading to droughts, and in southern Africa and eastern Brazil droughts also appear to coincide with Warm Events. Such correlations were especially noticeable during the disastrously persistent El Niño of 1982–83.

Climatic change or unusual weather may thus be due to natural activity a hemisphere away, just as a strong tropical jet stream developed in southern Asia can affect storm activity over the African Sahel (p.20). As it happens, a vigorous Indian monsoon often coincides with strong Westerlies in the middle latitudes.

Satellite observations of ocean surface conditions are valuable for long-term forecasting. As the strong Aghulas current is part of the regular oceanic circulation which transports much energy from the southern to northern hemisphere, monitoring its properties may aid long-term climatic predictions for parts of the northern Atlantic.

Ocean surfaces and cyclonic activity

Our ability to influence these great circulations might seem minimal, yet they respond to atmospheric warming. Sea-surface temperature increase seems to make for **more frequent and more intense cyclonic activity** in latitudes where the Coriolis force is effective and the ocean surface above 27°C. Since 1960 Fiji has experienced an increasing number of cyclones; during which time South Pacific surface temperatures have risen by about 0.2C°. Most have coincided with an El Niño event, though these have not been more frequent. If our activities *do* induce further air temperature rise and warmer seas, cyclones could become more intense and extend to higher latitudes in each hemisphere.

Sustained melting of Arctic pack-ice would affect ocean circulation and air moisture in high latitudes, with more variable weather and more intense storm activity bordering the North Atlantic – as yet there is little evidence of this happening. We *could* effect significant climatic changes, but, as always, it would depend on whether or not natural variations act to override our inputs.

- Explain why the atmosphere and oceans should be considered as part of a single system, remembering that the ocean's heat capacity is two thousand times that of the atmosphere.

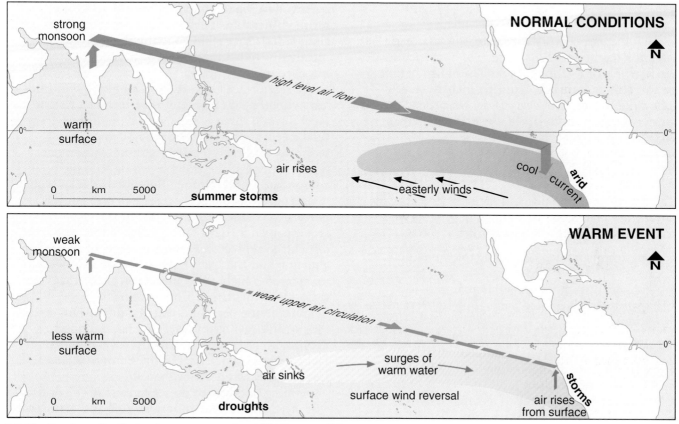

NORMAL CONDITIONS

N

strong monsoon

high level air flow

warm surface

air rises

cool current

arid

easterly winds

summer storms

0 km 5000

WARM EVENT

N

weak monsoon

weak upper air circulation

less warm surface

air sinks

surges of warm water

surface wind reversal

storms

air rises from surface

droughts

0 km 5000

2.5 The Southern Oscillation between normal and El Niño conditions.

2.6 As a tropical cyclone approached, a soaring convection current fed with energy from condensation carried this cloud thousands of metres above Puerto Rico in a matter of minutes.

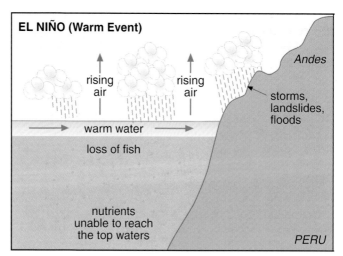

EL NIÑO (Warm Event)

Andes

rising air

rising air

storms, landslides, floods

warm water

loss of fish

nutrients unable to reach the top waters

PERU

2.7 Off the coast of Peru a blanket of warm water prevents nutrients reaching the surface, affecting marine life and the predatory birds. Unusual moisture brings heavy rainfall and flooding to normally arid coastlines (2.4).

RISING SEA-LEVEL – CONSIDERING CONSEQUENCES

Contributions to rising sea-level

During the past century expansion due to ocean warming has been the main cause of a mean annual sea-level rise of 1–2 mm. As expansion lags behind any air temperature rise, a further increase should follow. Predictions now vary widely but suggest, with greater inputs from ice-melt, a rise of some 20 cm by 2030.

Factors affecting possible consequences

The effects on coastlands and their settlements will differ from one region to another, depending on a combination of contributory factors:

- Long-term warming or cooling due to natural causes;
- Accelerated warming due to human activities;
- Expansion due to the oceanic time-lag response to warming;
- Increasing melt-water inputs or, countering this, higher snowfall and ice accumulation;
- Exceptional ice disintegration – possibly of the West Antarctic icesheet;
- Uplift or depression due to tectonic activity;
- Uplift due to post-glacial rebound – land about Hudson Bay has risen by a metre over the last century;
- Sea-bed depression due to extra water;
- Land subsidence due to sediment loading;
- Land subsidence due to liquid extraction;
- Land subsidence due to urbanisation;
- Coastal submergence due to storm surges – which even a small sea-level rise might amplify.

An exceptional rise over the next century seems unlikely. A slow increase, of the order of half a metre, is probable *if* predictions for global warming are borne out.

The consequences may vary widely

Developed countries may counter rises by using appropriate technology and financial sources to support preventive measures. Despite alarmist reports, it is unlikely that large parts of Britain's lowlands will be submerged. Apart from vigilant coastal protection, plans aim to counter surging, such as occurred during the 1953 North Sea flood, and forestall problems of up-river tidal extension.

Less developed countries would, as always, be **more vulnerable**. The over-populated lowlands of **Bangladesh** have suffered many flood disasters, mostly due to river overflow, sometimes to cyclone-impelled waves. Though vulnerable to any sea-level rise, a recent UN Disaster Programme Report finds **'no evidence that a greenhouse-induced rise in sea-level poses a threat'**.[4] The wide composite delta with tidal creeks is unstable, subject to depression by sediment load and to erratic tectonic movements. Small settlements lie along leveés or on more consolidated land. Normal flooding is shallow. The main concern is not sea-level rise per se, but the **periodic cyclones** from the Bay of Bengal, accompanied by devastating storm surges. It is difficult to protect this enormous area of shifting alluvium and changing levels with embankments many metres high. Of course, even a slight sea-level rise adds to the danger from surging.

Considering coastland vulnerability means assessing the possible rate of sea-level rise; natural uplift or depression, or that created by the local population. Heightening sea defences in the Long Beach area of **Los Angeles** was described recently as 'a response to impending flooding by an ice-fed rise of the oceans'. The article failed to mention that **oil and artesian water extraction** has, over half a century, created local subsidence of between 2–9 m!

Atolls are targeted as most likely to be submerged by sea-level rise. Again other considerations cloud the issue. These island rings, a metre or so above the ocean, have extended upwards and outwards in response to rising sea-level, or some to slow subsidence of a volcanic mount. Inland of their wide outer reefs, storms create protective beaches of limestone debris. The seaward reefs grow outwards, and exceptional storms realign the beach material so they survive. Their future obviously depends on the rate of sea-level rise, on tectonic movements, and on their location relative to storm occurrences. Each is a system which merits particular study. Certainly they are not all doomed, and description of seawater incursion affecting crop production on a particular atoll should not be taken as portraying inevitable disaster for atolls in general.

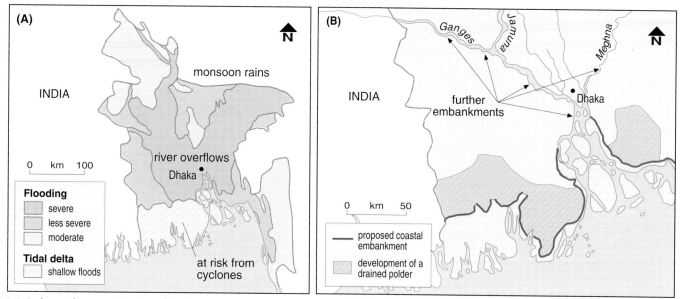

2.8 **A** shows the extensive river flooding in Bangladesh during the monsoon and extending delta lands exposed to cyclone-induced waves. A UN Development Project aims to control flooding through embankments, pumping, storages and draw-down before the monsoon. **B** shows a possible long-term project designed to protect 60 000 km² of drained delta land from exceptional surges.[5]

- Consider why, with the 1993 flood devastation in the Mississippi basin exaggerated by failures of protective banking, many feel that the Bangladesh project (2.8) is unsuitable, and that funding should be diverted to re-establishing coastal mangroves and providing suitable high-ground refuges.

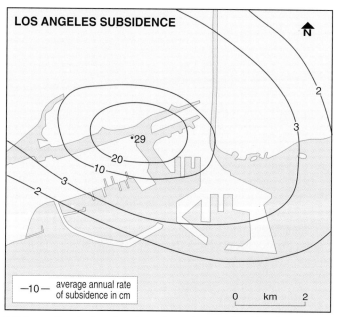

2.9 Long Beach, Los Angeles, where the coastland has long been subsiding due to oil and water extraction. The protective sea walls have recently been heightened.

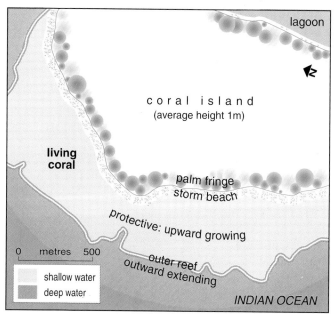

2.10 Waves break continuously on the edge of the outer reef of Gan Island, in an Equatorial Maldivian atoll. Occasional storm surges cross the shallows and reconstruct the protective storm beach.

3

CHANGES IN THE BIOSPHERE

- Plants and animal life – a delicate balance

- Tropical rainforest – disturbing the systems

- Consumer demands and deforestation

- Dry marginal lands – disturbance/resilience

- Agriculture – part of the biosphere

- Intensive farming – side-effects

- Technology for the developing word

A single fence can make all the difference.

The following pages examine some of the consequences of disturbing elements of our biotic environment, whether natural (primary) or secondary in origin. It is easy to hold a placard saying 'save the . . .', but usually very difficult to achieve absolute protection in view of conflicting interests. The ambition of under-privileged people to acquire apparently vacant territory is understandable, as is the fact that semi-nomadic pastoralists benefit their community by firing savanna to renew grazing, yet must disturb many natural associations amid the tree-grassland, like those in 3.1.

As the rapidly increasing populations of the less developed countries seek higher living standards, it is difficult to reconcile wildscape preservation and the needs of distressed communities. But many of the threats to natural species come from demands of developed nations a hemisphere away, and from commercial interests. These, too, may be difficult to control, though it is easier to challenge them from a moral standpoint. Even established rural landscapes are continuously changed, with an eye to potential gain, often by more intensive farming, which may bring immediate benefits but can also have unfortunate side-effects, as we shall see.

3.1 *(above)* Acacia savanna, with weaver-birds' nests beyond the reach of snakes, whose holes in the termite mound alert mongooses, who have worn a track about it.

3.2 *(below)* Traces of former shifting settlement near a seasonal stream amid the Tanzanian savanna. Tracks lead from the thatched houses and cattle enclosure (H) to an area burnt to provide fresh grazing (G).

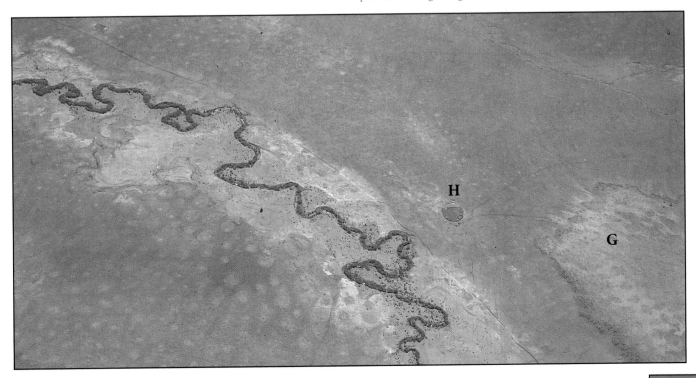

PLANT AND ANIMAL LIFE – A DELICATE BALANCE

In any mature form of vegetation there are delicate balances between living things. To appreciate how we are affecting rainforests or grasslands, we should examine the communities of plants and animals which co-exist in these large units of vegetation.

Plants – their immediate environment

Each plant survives in its own **micro-climatic and soil habitat** in competition with those about it. Leaves, stems, and roots grow under different physical conditions (3.3), their cells developing an appropriate size, shape, and chemical composition. Moisture also varies at different levels. On a still, clear night the ground rapidly loses heat, chilling the air in contact, whose moisture may condense as dew on the lower leaves. On a hot day air currents rise from the surface and rapid evaporation takes moisture from the leaves.

Plant organs adapt to local climatic and soil conditions. In dry locations deep-rooted plants have small leaves with thick tissues and waxy surfaces, their stomata (pores) protected from direct sunlight, or readily closing. By contrast, the floating stems and leaves of aquatic plants may contain sufficient air to keep stomata exposed to the atmosphere.

Balanced communities

Plant species compete for suitable light conditions. Beneath the leaf canopy of a rainforest different plants thrive at different levels, and **a balance between plant and animal species** develops in particular niches and at various heights. Plants are a prime food source, and certain animals thrive only if particular plants are available in sufficient quantity. The destruction of a single tree upsets the animal species it supports and also other communities about it (p.41). Unique species unable to adapt to the changed environment may not survive.

At the lowest level, **micro-organisms** provide chemicals in a form plants can absorb. Those on the roots of legumes such as beans or clovers convert atmospheric nitrogen into soluble compounds; others act to return nitrogen to the air. Various bacteria aid the decay of dead plant/animal material, allowing nutrients to be recycled through the vegetation.

Insects break down leaves and mix soils, birds and bats aid pollination, and birds of prey and larger animals keep down the numbers of smaller species –

living things acting to control each other in a balanced community in stable vegetation. So, before clearing plants or culling and managing particular animals, we should appreciate their exact role in the existing plant/animal community. Even small human interventions or climatic variations can cause a spectacular, sometimes disastrous, chain of events. A surge in the population of caterpillars, locusts or rabbits can strip vegetation and affect plant–soil relationships.

Disturbance and natural recovery

Among the common environmental hazards are the clearing and combustion of vegetation. However **large-scale burning** has long acted to create a natural balance between lifeforms over extensive areas. Much of the Australian 'bush' relies on periodic fires, often started by lightning, to recycle nutrients from the litter. Some plants regenerate only after fire (3.6).

The 'let it burn' policy in response to the Yellowstone fires in the USA, which in 1988 destroyed half a million hectares of forest, triggered an outcry from 'green' organisations. Yet fire is a natural part of the ecosystem, essential for re-seeding many pine species. Two years after, the soaring numbers of elk, bison, and other animals grazing the enriched and now well-lit food plants were threatening to exceed their pre-fire numbers, and may suddenly decline by outstripping resources.

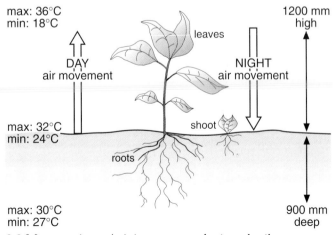

3.3 Mean maximum/minimum atmospheric and soil temperatures on an Indonesian farmland, which affect plant organs above and below ground.

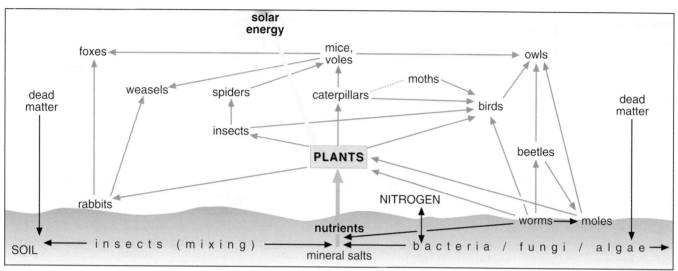

3.4 A simplified food web of a temperate woodland.

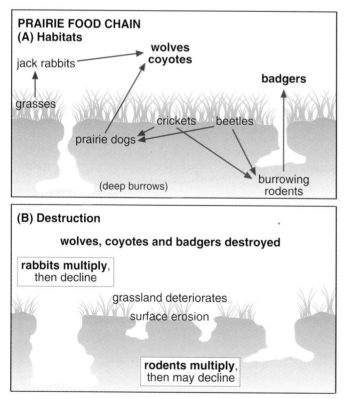

PRAIRIE FOOD CHAIN
(A) Habitats

(B) Destruction

wolves, coyotes and badgers destroyed

rabbits multiply, then decline

grassland deteriorates

surface erosion

rodents multiply, then may decline

3.5 A simplified balanced food web (**A**) on American prairie grassland suffers from the effects of destroying predators (**B**), which allowed a disastrously large population of rodents to degrade the landscape, lessening their own chances of survival.

- Consider possible consequences for other components of the food web in 3.4 of spraying to destroy caterpillars.

- After the Yellowstone fires the US National Parks Service revealed that 261 of some 40 000 large animals perished, also that soil heating rarely penetrated below 5–10 cm. How would these facts have affected their 'let it burn' decision?

3.6 Fires periodically sweep Western Australian bush, releasing nutrients and freeing seeds. These xanthorrhea with blackened stems rely on fire for regeneration.

Tropical forests vary with location

Tropical forests are rightly regarded as vegetation with unique characteristics which should be preserved; yet this is too simplistic a view. They are not uniform units of vegetation presenting similar attractions for settlers, timber firms, or plantation development, but **vary in composition and extent**. Broadleafed **evergreen forests** girdle the Equatorial regions, where humidity is high and rainfall abundant throughout the year, so that flowering, fruiting, and leaf-fall go on all the time. But there are also **tropical seasonal forests**, especially in the wet monsoon lands, where plants must survive a period of soil-water deficit. Many trees are deciduous so, with a seasonally incomplete leaf canopy, there is dense shrubby undergrowth and bamboo thickets.

Some forests are more likely to be cleared than others, sometimes with calamitous results; but the inference that forest clearance *must* lead to land degradation is far from the truth. Over the ages huge areas of tropical forest have been converted to closely settled productive agricultural land (3.12). Nevertheless, there are good reasons why the dwindling tropical forests should be preserved in their natural state.

Variations within the forests

The forests are **mosaics of small patches**, each with different combinations of plants – in south-east Asia there may be several hundred different tree species per hectare. Some **evergreen forests** are seasonally flooded, some on level interfluves, some on hillsides, their plant communities varying with the peaty soils in swamps, lateritic soils on higher, level ground, and the range of soils on slopes.

Each forest 'patch' supports **a complex community of plants and animals**, more or less stratified. Trees with broad leafy crowns 40–50 metres up emerge from a lower, more continuous canopy of tree crowns about 25–35 metres above the forest floor. These reflect or absorb most of the incoming light energy – perhaps a quarter reaching the younger trees and smaller species beneath. Plants near ground level receive only flecks of intense light. The water received by individual plants depends on exposure and location in respect of drips and trunk-flow.

Innumerable micro-climates make for **a great diversity of plant species** and forms. Epiphytes – ferns, orchids, bromeliads, and mosses – festoon branches at appropriate levels of light intensity and moisture. Lianas and other climbers wind upwards or loop-down and re-root themselves. Animals find their own levels according to habit and diet – from termites, essential for breaking-down plant litter, to climbing mammals, reptiles, and insects, with birds and bats at the highest levels. Their **mobility helps pollination** for, with such diversity, individual plant species are scattered through the forest.

Monsoon forest also shows layered variation, with massive emergent hardwoods like teak and sal often targeted for logging. Generally there is more branching but fewer epiphytes. Middle and lower levels include both deciduous and evergreens. Leaf litter, dry for long periods, decomposes more slowly. The behaviour of mammals, reptiles, and abundant insect life varies seasonally.

In all the tropical forests whenever unique plant-animal associations are disturbed they never exactly regain their former composition. Even though secondary forest re-covers a clearing, many original species will be absent.

Unpredictable effects of clearance

Clearing even a small patch creates **ripple effects**, for so many lifeforms are dependent on others. Epiphytes use nutrients from soil and litter transported by ants to build 'gardens' high among branches, and 3.8 shows a wider web of activity torn apart by felling a single tree. The cecropia's leaves feed the sloth, slow-moving and benefiting from camouflage provided by green algae in its hair-grooves. Moths help pollinate the tree and use sloth droppings and the algae as convenient food for developing larvae; they in turn are prey to lizards living on and about the tree. Omnivorous lemurs eat its seeds and catch lizards. Fierce Azteca ants, living in the trunk, guard food-plants in ant gardens, and attack all predators *except* those who, like the sloth, feed on the cecropia.

- Consider why exploiting a particular forest area in a certain way may not be possible in other parts of the broad area of rainforest, with its mosaic composition.

3.7 A rainforest emergent, host to a complex community of lifeforms, indicated by the variety of epiphytes and lianas using the tree to support themselves in a favourable environment.

- Why are frequent assertions that clearing tropical rainforest leads to land degradation far too sweeping?

- Consider why forecasting the future for a rainforest formation by extrapolating from clearance rates in a particular area is likely to be misleading.

- The most serious effect of rainforest clearance may be the loss of unique plant-animal associations. Consider why any particular association is unlikely to be found in other forested areas.

CECROPIA ECOSYSTEM

- **cut one tree and the ecosystem breaks down**

- **cut over a wide area and unique species may disappear**

Sloth depends on **this** particular tree species – the cecropia

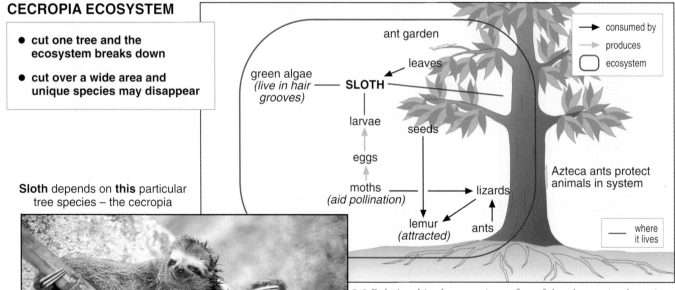

3.8 Relationships between just a few of the plant-animal species dependent on a Brazilian tree, the cecropia, isolated among the abundance of other trees.

3.9 A sloth in the Brazilian forest.

TROPICAL RAINFORESTS – THEIR PRESERVATION

Preserving the diversity

Low-latitude rainforests are the planet's greatest genetic pool, with diverse species developed uninterrupted over millions of years, though possibly modified during glacial periods. It is essential to preserve such wildlife species and maintain their biodiversity. **Tropical crops** – rice, bananas, papayas and many others – made high yielding by introducing appropriate genetic samples from wild species, are continually reproducing from a narrow genetic base, which weakens them in time. Their uniformity also exposes them to devastation by a particular disease. It is necessary to **reintroduce** original and related wild **genetic material**. This may be impossible should wild species be lost by natural forest destruction.

Common pharmaceutical products such as antibiotics and tranquillisers, originally developed from tropical forest plants, are now produced synthetically. Extracts from other plants are investigated for effectiveness in combating pests, controlling cancers, and curative purposes. Tropical rainforests contain about **half the planet's species of biota** yet relatively few have been studied in detail and **large numbers await indentification**. Unidentified **insects** may have similar potential. Indigenous people have long harvested insects for dyes, antibiotics, and medicines, many of which have since been developed synthetically. One Amazonian tree was found to harbour 1700 species of ant and beetle, apart from other animal life. Some insects, such as parasitic wasps, are used to control pests as substitutes for insecticides.

Gene banks in bio-diversity centres preserve species, but it is essential to safeguard as much natural rainforest as possible.

Maintaining natural cycles

Interactions between forest plants and the atmosphere include recycling processes involving local soils and nutrient circulations. As rainwater drips through leaves and runs down stems and trunks it carries the droppings and remains of myriad animals which are soaked up and decomposed in the soil. Little water runs off the litter-strewn surface. **The nutrients are rapidly recycled**, in solution, and water returned to the air by direct evaporation and evapotranspiration. Half the rain received may be locally recycled water.

The soils, not rich in themselves, **act as vehicles** which maintain nutrient exchanges. Clearance exposes and dries them, allowing nutrients, even those added by burning, to be carried by run-off to the streams, together with loosened soil particles. Unless there is careful reforestation or agricultural management, particles may infill streams, naturally clear of chemical content and sediment load, and cause flooding. Not all cleared land becomes waste, but sound traditional or technological methods are needed to provide a stable substitute vegetation; and so much clearing today is haphazard.

Some see forest clearance causing **climatic change** on a global scale, partly because of increasing atmospheric carbon dioxide. They envisage the destruction of entire rainforests, like that covering Amazonia, assuming that current clearance will continue at an exponential rate. Clearance *is* devastating parts of Amazonia, but not overall. Also widespread climatic consequences are even less easy to predict as other vegetation becomes established.

The preservation of forest communities

Interference with indigenous communities occupying traditional forest territory occurs for many reasons. Indonesia has encouraged millions of Javanese to move to Sumatra and Kalimantan, displacing indigenous peoples as they clear the forests (p.46). Similar settlement in Irian Jaya has involved clashes with hunter-gatheres, whose age-old, distinctive culture is destroyed by moving them to tin-shack settlements.

In Amazonia threats come from logging, mining, dam-building, ranching, and haphazard settlements. The indigenous people are widely scattered. Some hunter-gatherers maintain an independent life, but many have become appendages to poor communities of migrant settlers or prospectors, with problems from disease and cultural-shock.

Even when tribal boundaries are agreed, contact with outsiders erodes former traditions and ways of life. Agencies protecting their interests find that medical help and simple practical gifts, such as machetes, may stimulate a desire for commercial products. Trying to ensure complete isolation is apt to create a 'zoo' situation.

Others, successfully settled amid rainforest, feel that developed nations prospering from tropical produce derived from forest genetic material put little back to enhance living standards at the source.

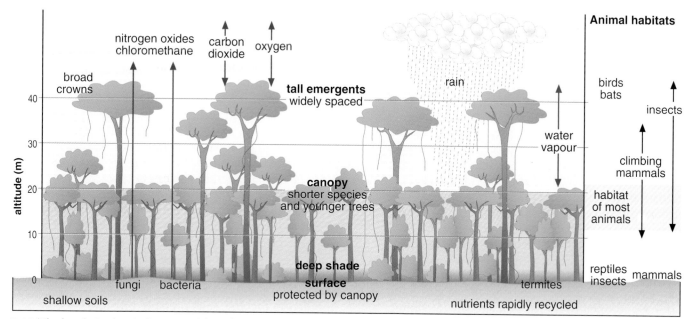

Animal habitats

nitrogen oxides
chloromethane

carbon dioxide

oxygen

broad crowns

tall emergents
widely spaced

rain

birds
bats

insects

water vapour

climbing mammals

canopy
shorter species
and younger trees

habitat of most animals

altitude (m)

deep shade
surface
protected by canopy

reptiles
insects

mammals

fungi   bacteria

termites

shallow soils

nutrients rapidly recycled

3.10 The low-latitude rainforest – a delicately balanced system, vulnerable to disturbance.

- Half the atmospheric nitrous oxide is released from tropical rainforest. Consider why forest clearance should act to preserve stratospheric ozone, warm the stratosphere, and perhaps lower global surface temperatures.

- Should our main concern about deforestation focus on local environmental disruption or on wider threats to the global system?

3.11 For its abundant growth the Brazilian rainforest depends on nutrient cycling processes in the shallow soil layer covering the deep clayey regolith above the weathering rock. Once disturbed, careful management is needed (3.12).

3.12 The Ayung valley in Bali, cleared of original forest, with rice, palms, cassava and other crops productively managed in harmony with natural conditions.

CONSUMER DEMANDS AND DEFORESTATION

Demands for timber products

Genetic improvements from forest resources serve everyone, but developed countries benefiting from their commercial products might be expected to fund schemes to preserve primary forest, especially as their other demands cause immense damage. Extracting suitable, widely dispersed **tropical hardwoods** for furniture, panelling, and parquet floors disturbs large areas of forest. Other species are felled in bulk for plywood, doors or scaffolding used by urban-industrial societies. Japan uses over three-quarters of imported tropical logs for such purposes. Timber prices, responding to increasing demands, make logging **profitable for developing countries** with exploitable forest. The concessions granted to foreign timber companies have limitations on extraction rates and which trees can be felled, but they are difficult to enforce and open to corruption and illicit logging. Regeneration time for natural species is usually longer than the period granted to the companies, during which they cut the area only once to get maximum short-term value, with scant concern for long-term effects.

Selective felling should mean minimum disturbance of the ecosystem and indigenous people, with replanting and time for other species to recover. In practice, felling and heavy machinery damage adjacent vegetation and impede regrowth of original species, so that rapidly growing secondary vegetation, with vines and climbers, takes over. **Access roads** cause damage and open the forest to casual settlers and loggers. Working a tenth frequently destroys half the remaining forest.

Tree plantations and agro-forestry

New **plantations** are sometimes established over cleared forest, using species which may meet demands for timber, or even local firewood, and preserve forest elsewhere. In south-east Asia **rapidly maturing species** of eucalypt, pine, and acacia are felled or coppiced. Unfortunately pests can reach epidemic proportions in simplified ecosystems. Some estates plant adjacent stands of different species and varying age to combat this. **Crops grown between tree-lines** control erosion and trap organic debris, though eucalypts produce acidic litter and need so much water that soils become dry and acidified – even nearby crops show reduced yields.

Consumer demands – indirect effects

Increasing demand for **fast foods** like hamburgers has stimulated widespread conversion of Central American rainforest to unstable pasture, capable for a while of providing cheap beef for consumers of cheap produce. European countries seeking **cheap livestock feed** import and process large quantities of cassava for pigs, cattle and poultry. Thailand, by clearing forests, has become a major supplier. With such commercial interests and the lack of awareness of average consumers, it is difficult to create voluntary cut-back in demand. It requires regulations to **control imports or cut consumption**, perhaps by taxes imposed on tropical agricultural produce or wood. Developing countries might seek compensation for reduced export earnings, though would not necessarily fund alternatives to forest clearance, especially where population increase puts pressure on land.

Encouraging or subsidising temperate hardwood production, and allowing **temperate timber** products onto world markets at low rates, might ease pressure on tropical forests, but developing countries are sensitive to 'unfair' competition from those who have already destroyed their *own* natural habitats. Protecting forest in return for **writing off debt** is being undertaken in some cases (p.82). Political moves to conserve primary forest often leave loopholes. In 1989 Thailand, with the highest deforestation rate in south-east Asia, banned logging. Its forests contain valuable hardwoods like teak and sal. However, untitled settlers have even been clearing forest reserves, so that reforestation is difficult without displacing communities. Also to maintain supplies Thai companies have agreements with Myanma and Laos to exploit *their* timber reserves . . . so the depletion continues.

- Summarise the variety of consumer demands which directly and indirectly put pressure on tropical rainforests. What kind of publicity might induce a concerned response from a consuming public largely unaware of the consequences?

- Comment on the dilemma facing those who would prevent high-consuming societies from importing tropical timber products.

3.13 Soil erosion here was rapid as Caribbean forest was cleared to provide small-holdings. Five years later these gulleys were hip-deep; but subsequent collapse, with mineral mixing and plant nutrients washed in, has allowed secondary growth to cover this broken surface.

3.14 The use of machinery, and tracks cleared for selective felling, emphasise that rainforest disturbance may affect five times the actual area felled.

- Consider why industrially developed nations and developing countries in the low latitudes are likely to approach rainforest conservation from very different viewpoints.

- Notice how 3.14 and 3.15 illustrate that pressures on natural vegetation are both direct and indirect, local and global. Why does the natural composition of low-latitude rainforest mean that the effects of lumbering are likely to be widespread?

3.15 Overseas demands for pastoral products and their importance to the national economy, are indirectly responsible for the erosion of these New Zealand hillsides, cleared for grazing.

Colonisation – assisted and haphazard

Surveys in south-east Asia have shown that extracting 20 trees per hectare may damage over half the remaining 400 or so beyond recovery. Such losses could be reduced by international agreements and timber companies' co-operation. It is much more difficult to control forest clearance by millions of landless families from overcrowded cities and overpopulated rural areas. The rapid growth of world population threatens the forest both by the numbers seeking land and additional consumers demanding produce. Primary forest is being colonised with assistance from governments and by haphazard migrations.

Population pressure

Java, an island of 13 000 km², has a dense rural population – over a hundred million, half under 20 years old. Continuous migration to urban areas creates shanties with inadequate facilities, adding particularly to Jakarta's 8 million inhabitants. During the 1980s **the government assisted over 3 million to migrate** to Indonesia's outer islands, especially to Sumatra, Kalimantan, and Irian Java. Sumatra's coastal swamps suit rice cultivation, but most migrants, provided with basic equipment, opted to clear rainforest. Far from markets, many struggle for a living as soils deteriorate, while indigenous shifting cultivators resent loss of territory and the apparent privileged treatment of newcomers.

The costly assisted settlement has been cut back, though migration continues and successful settlers extend their inroads. Migrants may be blamed for forest destruction and disrupting tribal communities, but the real problem is how Java can cope with over two million extra people a year. Encouraging birth control and financing rural improvements cannot guarantee success, even in the long term.

The attraction of 'empty spaces'

Almost three-quarters of Brazil's population is landless, including millions of rural families. Of the land-holders, less than ten per cent control almost half the cultivated area. As the overcrowded cities embrace numerous shanty settlements, it is not surprising that Brazil and adjoining countries regard **the Amazon forests**, which cover some 5×10^6 km², **as under-used**.

To increase Amazonia's contribution to the economy, the government aims to extract such minerals as iron ore, manganese, bauxite, tin, and gold, increase timber exports, create dams for hydro-electricity, and provide access to areas deemed suitable for large-scale pastoral or agricultural settlement. There have already been disastrous side-effects. The huge Carajas iron ore project, a successful export venture, has spawned iron ore smelters which plunder the forest for charcoal for cheap fuel. Gold fever entices hundreds of thousands of poor hopefuls to widespread alluvial workings, mostly illegal, polluting rivers with mercury and wastes and introducing diseases against which tribal people have no resistance. Outside pressures have restricted projects for 160 dams likely to flood tribal lands, but almost half are still envisaged.

Upgrading a 1400 km highway has brought disaster to **rainforests in Rondônia** (3.16). Floods of settlers have burned and cleared forest about rough feeder roads. As soil fertility declines many plots are acquired by cattle ranches, some of which have survived barely a decade. Many families *have* prospered and much pastoral land is stable, but since the 1970s the rate of clearance has increased and reserves and conservation areas are frequently breached. Perhaps a sixth of the indigenous people remain.

Other Amazonian forests face similar treatment, especially in eastern Ecuador where access roads accompany petroleum extraction. Even so, **it is unwise to focus on a particular area and extrapolate the extent and rate of disturbance to predict the future for Amazonia as a whole**. Recent 'green' predictions that much of the Amazon rainforest will have been obliterated by the turn of the century are unhelpful, to put it mildly. Vast areas of remaining forest are not affected in the same way. Nevertheless, while such threats persist, at the least land-use schemes must include planned forest reserves and safeguards for the indigenous population.

- Consider the extent to which the pressure on the tropical rainforest comes from the composition, social structure, and behaviour of populations far removed from the forests themselves.

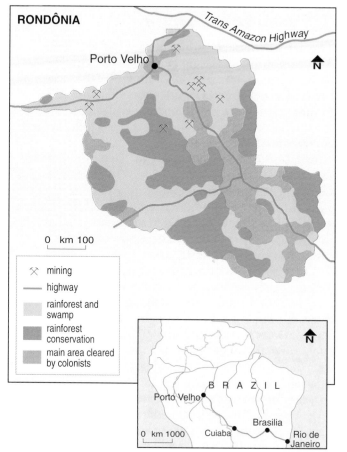

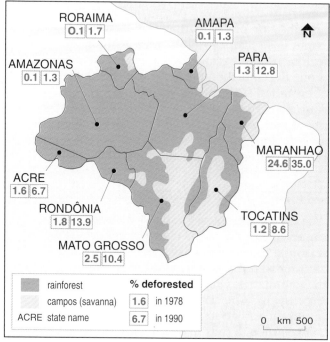

3.18 Each State shows increasing interference with rainforest, though not on the scale of Rondônia and Para. Rainforest is still extensive, with over 98 per cent of the north and west untouched.

3.16 The highway extended westward from Cuiaba allowed extensive deforestation in Rondônia, and incursions continued into Conservation Areas and AmerIndian reserves.

3.17 Tropical countries with rapid population growth are likely to extend settlement into rainforest and profit from felling, as here in Sri Lanka.

There are many imponderables to assess and priorities to consider regarding the future of tropical rainforests:

- The preservation of unique ecosystems – how much primary forest should be conserved and where?

- What are the justifications for allowing rural landless and urban squatters to colonise 'unused' forest?

- Need forest clearance create wasteland, as often alleged?

- Could extraction of forest produce be restricted to benefit local people?

- Would absolute isolation benefit most indigenous people? How best are their interests safeguarded?

- Most consumers are not aware that certain cheap commodities endanger rainforest. How can this be countered?

- Should the global climatic consequences of forest removal be a major concern?

47

DRY MARGINAL LANDS – DETERIORATION UNDER PRESSURE

Desertification is used to describe a progressive deterioration of dry marginal lands, whose global extent is discussed overleaf. They include semi-arid regions bordering lands of greater productivity but prone to population pressure, such as the dry margins of savannas, steppes, the Mediterranean lands, and the Australian 'bush'. Deterioration of soils and vegetation also occurs, of course, amid more favourable parts of these regions, and incipient degradation of savanna is common about semi-permanent settlements.

Savannas – productive but precarious

The extent of tropical grassland-with-trees is not simply a response to the climatic regime – hot rainy season(s) then lengthy dry season(s). Burning and clearing adjacent woodland extends savanna and blurs the boundaries, while the semi-arid margins are even less easy to define with climatic fluctuations and uncertain human responses.

Even though soils may be poor, most **savannas have a high primary productivity**. Grasses have shallow, branched root systems, enabling them to grow quickly with the rains and support abundant wildlife and herds. In dry areas they rapidly extract water, so it is difficult for woody plants to develop. Fires, some natural, some lit to encourage nutritious grass growth, sweep the savanna during the dry season. Most trees and shrubs are fire-resistant, and survive drought by shedding leaves. In Africa herds of wildebeest, zebra, and gazelle migrate with the rains and fresh grass growth; other animals browse, giraffe taking top leaves of trees and shrubs, rhino the lower shoots. It all seems remarkably stable, yet these **associations are easily unbalanced** by climatic fluctuation or human mismanagement, and soils deteriorate; though the speed of recovery is often astonishing.

Herdsmen from semi-permanent settlements move cattle over established territory, while their families maintain subsistence cultivation, graze cattle, and herd goats which browse locally on shrubs and young trees. Firewood gathering is continuous, though dwindling supplies means lopping branches and up-rooting shrubs. As cropped land loses nutrients, these joint threats to soils and vegetation are eased by shifting settlements – extending the area under threat. **Population increase puts more pressure on resources**. Some countries restrict semi-nomadic movements; but with an erratic climate settled farming is a precarious alternative.

The semi-arid margins

The dry Sahel, between the Sahara and the West African savanna, has long been sparsely populated, with semi-nomadic herdsmen moving cattle seasonally between water sources. With drought, some retreated to more settled areas, while many concentrated on the more reliable wells, and though this led to local land degradation losses were small.

In recent times severe droughts have caused great suffering and immense losses of livestock. Some suggest that atmospheric pollution and consequent climatic change could be acting to extend deserts worldwide – the theme of 'desertification'. Whatever the reasons, other circumstances now make for disaster in these semi-arid lands, stretching from Ethiopia to the Atlantic. Over the centuries periods of average or above-average rainfall *have* followed decade-long drought, and adequate grazing has been re-established over desert margins. But now **populations are rapidly increasing** in the countries concerned (p.81), so years of apparent bounty find ever more pastoralists establishing themselves, boring new wells and increasing herds. **The inevitable return to years of drought takes a greater toll**. Families retreating southward put pressure on soil and fuel resources among marginal settlements, themselves more densely populated, and land degradation spreads.

In most of these marginal lands conditions depend on climatic variability and the efficiency of traditional activities. Even though it is possible to **adopt new technology**, introduce protective tree belts, irrigation, soil improvement, or new crop species, success depends on injections of know-how and funding from government or international sources. Past successes have transformed many semi-arid lands, like the well-established, irrigated farmlands of the Punjab. HYV crops now benefit many communities in dry parts of south-east Asia. Unfortunately political pressures for immediate action and lack of long-term planning can create environmental disasters like the expanding wastelands south of the Aral Sea.

- Consider the future of lands like the Sahel. Will population pressures increase? Is atmospheric pollution increasing drought? Can traditional pastoral activities survive? Are large-scale developments – tree-belts, irrigation schemes – feasible, or would funding intermediate technological devices (e.g. alternative fuel sources) be preferable? Much depends on political stability.

3.19 Despoiled vegetation where restrictions on movement put pressure on the environment about Maasai communities.

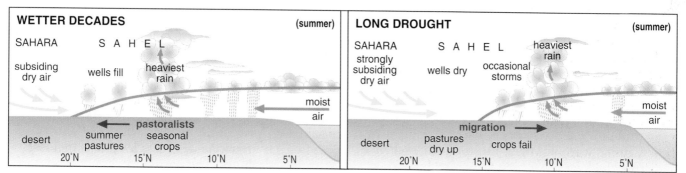

WETTER DECADES	(summer)
SAHARA	S A H E L

subsiding dry air — wells fill — heaviest rain

moist air

desert — summer pastures — seasonal crops

← pastoralists

20°N — 15°N — 10°N — 5°N

LONG DROUGHT	(summer)
SAHARA	S A H E L	heaviest rain

strongly subsiding dry air — wells dry — occasional storms

moist air

desert — pastures dry up — crops fail

migration →

20°N — 15°N — 10°N — 5°N

3.20 Successive years of adequate summer rain encourage temporary settlements in dry marginal lands; abandoned as drought forces families and livestock to migrate southwards.

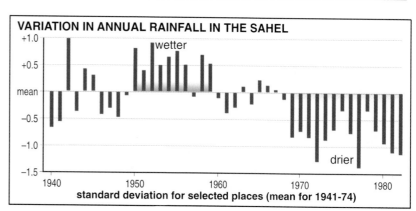

VARIATION IN ANNUAL RAINFALL IN THE SAHEL

wetter

drier

+1.0
+0.5
mean
−0.5
−1.0
−1.5

1940   1950   1960   1970   1980

standard deviation for selected places (mean for 1941-74)

3.21 Erratic rainfall and lengthy drought have occurred over the centuries, but now the populations affected have increased.

RESILIENCE; RECOVERY; DESERTIFICATION

Land degradation

Deforestation, over-grazing, or firewood plundering affect the soil structure, and subsequent effects of wind and water may cause surface degradation. **Fragile environments in semi-arid lands** are at particular risk during lengthy drought. As people abandon dry wells, exposed crumbling soils and over-grazed pasture, the desert appears to be taking over. In the areas to which they migrate, land degradation may follow as they and their animals concentrate about scarce water sources.

If drought continues, the immediate effects act to intensify others. Dry soils cannot release sufficient moisture to encourage cloud formation. Bare surfaces reflect more incoming energy, reducing convectional updraughts. Loosened soils release more dust, which may also increase radiative cooking. Such conditions tend to allow upper air to subside, which in itself intensifies drought. The idea that drought may be self-perpetuating has reinforced the belief that there is increasing, widespread desertification – that the world's deserts are inexorably advancing. It is important therefore to distinguish clearly between circumstances in which land becomes degraded yet may recover and those which create surface conditions with no such resilience, no natural recovery – part of a true desert.

Resilience and recovery

Desertification is widely pictured as masses of dust and sand moving to smother fringe settlements, the result of declining rainfall and human mismanagement. Statistics are put forward to show desert conditions annually extending over millions of hectares of the world's surface. But **the resilience of many marginal areas** has been too easily discounted.

Prolonged drought, as in the Sahel, induces research during very dry periods. In the 1970s ecologists asserted that the southern Saharan desert, having advanced some 100 km in the last 15 years, would continue to do so at a rate of 6 km a year. Ten years later researchers in the same area revealed that no long-lasting desert conditions had been established, and that a fast land-production recovery had followed the Sahelian drought[6]. Boundaries between vegetation associations were as they had been 60 years before, with no eradication of woody species. A year later in Mali geographers observed that after the first good rains for five years sufficient vegetation

had re-established pasture over sand-covered areas.

The severity of recent droughts has enabled many semi-nomadic communities, during enforced short-term migrations, to learn to adopt **rick-aversion strategies**, such as keeping more manageable herds and using drought-tolerant crop variaties with tilling techniques better suited to dry soils.

The ability to effect recovery depends on available technology, backed by adequate funding. Back in the 1930s the return to productivity of land degraded in the Dust Bowl on the American plainlands required scientific inputs, crop substitution, appropriate machinery, and continuing innovations such as today's centre-pivot irrigation. But severe degradation is more of **a problem for people with limited resources** and without technological knowledge and equipment for restoration. Reclamation takes time, even with outside assistance, yet drought-stricken land frequently proves to be so resilient that desert fringes advance with drought and retreat with rainfall.

True deserts – their extent

The location and extent of the world's deserts relate mainly to relative positions of the landmasses and oceans, and to patterns of upper air circulation which make for air subsidence and dry surface conditions in particular regions. Aridity also occurs in rain-shadow areas and the heart of landmasses.

Any extensive long-term advance of the deserts is likely to be a response to changing global air circulation, ocean surface variations, or fluctuations in solar energy inputs, rather than to maltreatment of vegetation and soils on the desert fringes.[7] Severe land degradation certainly occurs there, but **the term desertification should be used with caution**.

Some see advancing deserts as inevitable if global warming continues. The possibility that, instead, many of the present desert margins would benefit from increased rainfall is considered on p.20.

- In southern Sudan vegetation on land about wells which had been able to sustain retreating herdsmen, and had shown serious effects of trampling, recovered particularly rapidly with the onset of rains. Consider why.

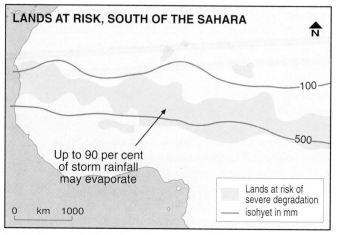

LANDS AT RISK, SOUTH OF THE SAHARA

N

—100—

—500—

Up to 90 per cent
of storm rainfall
may evaporate

Lands at risk of
severe degradation
isohyet in mm

0   km   1000

3.22 The marginal lands with erratic rainfall, high evaporation, and population pressure on soils.

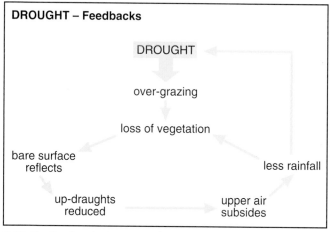

DROUGHT – Feedbacks

DROUGHT

over-grazing

loss of vegetation

bare surface
reflects

less rainfall

up-draughts
reduced

upper air
subsides

3.23 Feedbacks which may prolong drought; though this depends on the scale, and on the general atmospheric conditions.

- Annual rainfall statistics are of little value when considering the ability of dry land to recover. Consider this in view of the physiological adaptations of plants and animals, their habits, and the fact that seeds may lie dormant for years. Why is it necessary to monitor ground conditions over several decades before considering the spread of 'desertification'?

3.24 Dry water courses and bare fields about an Eritrean village during prolonged drought in the early 1970s.

3.25 Drought broke temporarily in 1975, greening these Eritrean hillsides and showing the resilience of these marginal areas.

AGRICULTURE AS PART OF THE BIOSPHERE

Atlases present maps of 'natural vegetation' – areas of broad-leafed deciduous forest covering north-west Europe and grassland extending from Uruguay across the Argentine pampas; but all these zones of natural vegetation have been tampered with, and some scarcely exist as such. **Agriculture** has replaced most mid-latitude forests and grasslands, and we have seen how tropical forests and savannas are subject to human interference. Much rainforest accepted as 'natural' is in fact **secondary vegetation**, for shifting tribal groups have interfered with former plant associations but allowed forest regeneration, as in much of peninsular Malaysia.

Replacement need not be disastrous

It is often assumed that forest clearance must cause landscape degradation and significantly affect the climate. Certainly it means losing original species and changing soil structures and micro-climates; but it is in people's interest to create stable plant–soil relationships, and this has occurred over much formerly forested land. In eastern Asia carefully terraced cropped land has long replaced enormous areas of forest. Climatic changes **on a global scale** related to any particular agricultural development are difficult to establish, even to a minor degree.

Where ricefields or rubber plantations have replaced forest (3.26) or wheat covers former grassland, there are still exchanges of water vapour, carbon dioxide, and oxygen with the atmosphere. Some undesirable gases may be released, such as methane from ricefields or from huge herds of cattle, but on the whole **well-managed agricultural land remains a stable part of the biosphere**.

Mismanagement is another matter

Threats to the environment come from mismanagement of land, unwisely cleared or improperly cultivated. Ignorance, greed or, sadly, poverty linked to population pressures, create environmental problems.

In many cases natural vegetation has created and protected soils of sufficient fertility to tempt people to exploit what is really a fragile environment. **The loess lands of north-western China**, which once bore vegetation ranging from woodland to a grass-shrub covering, have suffered severe erosion. Their potential fertility, and the need for wood fuel in a region with bitterly cold winters, led to their clearance and the exposure of the fine, loose particles to wind and summer rain. Vast quantities are lost in dust storms, or removed down widening gullies to supply the Huang He with a load responsible for its name – The Yellow River. This has occurred over thousands of years on a scale which certainly affects local climatic conditions. Reforestation is taking place, with large-scale shelter-belts, and steps to control run-off from elaborately terraced hillsides. The vulnerability of other marginal regions is emphasised on p.48.

Simplifying natural associations

Agricultural land, part of the biotic environment, supports associations which are a simplification of the abundance and variety of the natural plants and associated animals and insects. The destruction of hedgerows, for instance, means a loss of bird life and small animals which exercised control over the territory about them. One of the reasons for replacing them is to support wildlife which can control crop pests.

The effects of simplification can be wide-ranging. The destruction of forests in Central America has interfered with the winter habitat of birds migrating from North America. Farmers in the southern prairies have found that as the population of these insect-eating birds has been reduced, crop pests have multiplied, and so have taken to using more pesticides, which have undesirable side-effects.

Preserving genetic diversity

The replacement of natural vegetation with simplified associations or by monoculture can lead to genetic problems. Cultivated plants and farm animals developed from wild stock gradually offer lower resistance to insects and viruses, and infections spread rapidly through them. It is necessary to preserve wild stock with genetic variation spread through a diverse plant and animal population from which to re-introduce desirable qualities. Artificial **genetic pools** are being established, but **the preservation of the natural habitat** is preferable, and is likely, of course, to include associations of plant and animal species with beneficial properties as yet unknown – unused wild species of great potential.

3.26 In Sri Lanka rainforest has been replaced by a managed landscape of ricefields, kikul palms, cassava, citrus, spices, and bananas – beyond are rubber plantations.

- The contrasting landscapes in 3.26, 3.27 and 3.28 illustrate that cultivation calls for a complete understanding of the relationships between climate, rock structure, soils, and vegetation within a region. Consider how they also show that successful agriculture may depend on appreciating conditions far beyond the locality itself, and that a failure to understand natural processes, even in a technologically developed society, can be disastrous.

3.27 Failure to appreciate natural processes has left once-fertile fields in the Indus valley salt-caked, as water, rising under pressure from irrigation water-levels upstream, evaporates.

3.28 Clearing the thick loess deposits of northern China of vegetation over the ages has caused immense gulleying. With summer rains, streams like this are choked with particles and farmers struggle to retain terraced fields.

SIDE-EFFECTS OF INTENSIVE FARMING

Intensive farming to make land as productive as possible has undesirable side-effects. After 1940 Britain needed to cultivate any soil of reasonable quality. Hedgerows were removed to create fields large enough for machine operations, which included distributing chemical fertilisers and pesticides, and access paths made to machine sheds and storage barns in an efficient, if environmentally unattractive, landscape. It created ecological problems which still persist.

Fertilisers and ecological effects

Once, nitrogen removed from the air by natural vegetation roughly balanced that returned by denitifying bacteria. Now nitrogen fixed by legumes and applied in fertilisers synthesised from atmospheric nitrogen exceeds that fixed by natural processes; together they greatly exceed that returned naturally to the air. On a global scale the effects of such imbalance are difficult to forecast, but locally the increasing use of nitrate fertilisers, successfully boosting crop yields, causes many problems.

Nitrates are very soluble. They reach streams and lakes both by leaching through the soil and by wash from the surface. They benefit aquatic as well as terrestrial plants, so that algae and water plants can become so dense through **eutrophication** that they shade out other organisms, and the subsequent rotting mass uses up oxygen needed by fish and other lifeforms. Cattle dung and sewage sludge distributed mechanically, increase nitrate concentration in the fields.

Phosphate, a component of many fertilisers, is adsorbed by soil particles and not easily removed by leaching. It reaches streams in solution from dung and treated sewage, and directly from domestic detergents and industrial wastes, again triggering eutrophication.

High nitrate ion concentration in drinking water affects the oxygen-carrying capacity of the blood, hazardous for young children (though in the UK the incidence of related conditions is very low). Agreed safe limits of nitrate concentration in potential drinking water are closely monitored.

Farm practices can reduce nitrate movement to streams by minimising soil disturbance, careful application at selected growth-periods and restricting additions on steep slopes or near streams. An autumn crop absorbs nitrogen left after summer harvest and reduces outwash when evaporation is low.

Whether **'organic farming'** helps in this respect is debatable – much leached nitrate comes from organic sources. It makes for soil stability and avoids pesticides but may not match the productivity achieved with artificial fertilisers.

Pesticides and alternatives

The use of pesticides, herbicides, insecticides, fungicides, and fumigants like methyl bromide, mostly applied by spraying, increases by some 10 per cent annually. Pesticides seeping into groundwater, rivers, and oceans may appear dispersed, but become concentrated in organic tissues in food chains (2.2), endangering aquatic life and human health. **Biological controls** are sometimes effective. Screwworm-fly populations (cattle pests) have been reduced by introducing irradiated sterile male flies. Insect parasites may be used in some cases.

In many tropical countries where pests multiply rapidly there is less control over pesticide use or guidance over suitability. Applications have killed predators as well as pests and so increased infestation.

Interfering with natural habitats

Intensive agriculture which has replaced woodlands, wetlands, heath, or flora-rich grazing land is certainly undesirable in countries with agricultural surpluses. Subsidising the setting aside of land, planting woodland, and encouraging forestry are welcome if environmentally suitable vegetation is substituted, and it is not subject to enforced rotation; though huge stands of conifers have undesirable effects and, in contrast to native broadleaf species, may reduce the habitat diversity of wildlife.

- 3.31 shows how soil nitrogen concentration is maintained by natural and artificial inputs, through complex exchanges between air, soil, water and soil organisms, with the help of aeration and drainage. Fertilisers are not environmental enemies in themselves. In the USA large-scale applications of artificial fertilisers make extensive farming more productive. Consider the pros and cons of such intensification.

- Outline the environmental problems caused by bureaucratic insistence on periodic rotation of set aside and farmed fields.

3.29 Algae blooms cover drainage canals fed by nitrates from these cattle pastures in the Netherlands.

3.30 Hedgeless fields in East Anglia exposed to wind erosion and with downslope seepage to drainage canals.

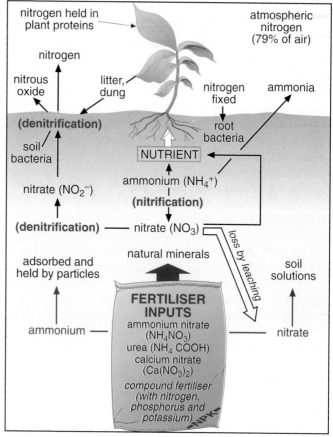

3.31 The complex movements of nitrogen between the atmosphere and soils containing natural and artificial nutrients.

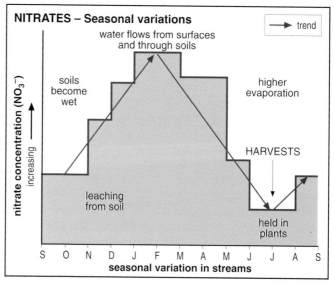

3.32 Seasonal management of farm activities can help to regulate nitrogen concentration in streams.

Introducing new technology

Introducing technology to improve crop yields and benefit livestock, aimed at alleviating rural poverty in overpopulated developing countries, seems a positive approach. Yet creating more intensive land use requires more efficient equipment, more energy inputs, and meeting the needs of new crop varieties or animal strains. This involves encouragement to abandon traditional practices and introducing credit arrangements at personal, community, and government levels. The Green Revolution has shown that such **changes can cause social and environmental problems.**

In monsoon Asia peasant farming, using simple technology and low energy inputs, could efficiently produce two annual rice crops to support several hundred people per square kilometre; but as the population density increased the yields were inadequate, and more marginal land was used. In the 1960s high-yielding varieties of rice (**HYVs**) were developed, requiring herbicides, pesticides, fertilisers and much water. For those who could afford them, mainly large landholders with favourable soils and reliable irrigation, yields more than doubled; but market prices for rice increased, creating much social unrest. Also HYVs were not suitable for marginal land with poorer irrigation facilities, and many subsistence farmers were unwilling to take the risk, even where credit could be obtained.

Since the mid-1970s research has provided varieties to suit particular conditions. As more effective credit schemes allowed purchases of seeds and fertilisers and irrigation improvements, poorer communities began to take them up, and the general increase in yields acted to bring down prices.

Sustainable development?

Some feel that such inputs cause traditional societies to decline, as activities are regulated by commercial interests and centralised government, and that technological innovations stimulate population growth, with unsustainable use of local resources, making for environmental degradation. They advocate a return to traditional practices with sustainable development on a community (village) basis, and envisage community-owned land increasing productivity through management of crops, animals, water, grazing, and trees as **a village ecosystem.**

In practice, activities of most rural populations have long been constrained by land tenure, private ownership, centralised government, and, in India, by age-old divisions of class and caste. Villagers are usually aware of the value of technological innovations, as in northern India where electric tube-wells back up canal systems and the overall increase in food production is seen to prevent major famines.

Using appropriate technology

Introducing advanced technology does not necessarily bring benefits. What is appropriate for one country may not be suitable for another. High-yielding Friesian cattle sent to Ethiopia and other East African countries failed to produce effectively, due to climate, diseases, and unsuitable feeds. Help in developing local breeds which could also be used for ploughing might have been preferable. Heavy machinery, too, is often unsuitable for village farmers. In tropical conditions it may compact wet soils, or in dry ones break up shallow, water-holding layers. Simple machinery or traditional implements are often more suitable. In parts of Mali, where imported machine pumps perpetually lack fuel and spare parts, carefully researched methods of soil retention and water collection using local implements are now effective.

China stresses the value of **intermediate technology**. Rural implements, hand-carts, and small all-purpose, fuel-saving tractors are maintained with careful efficiency, though family groups may now co-operate and share heavier machinery on amalgamated properties. Rural wastes are widely converted to gas energy in bio-converters (p.66).

High technology – a boon or a threat?

China improved rice varieties and fertilisation techniques over a thousand years ago, and has now developed varieties adapted to regional light conditions (3.33). In many countries genetic scientists are making food crops resistant to diseases, drought, salinity, or whatever. **Biotechnology** is used to clone plants and produce crops from minute tissues of those with suitable characteristics, avoiding natural hazards which hamper production in tropical countries. There are already substitutes for sugar, cocoa-butter, and vegetable oils. Unfortunately, large-scale production could adversely affect the economies and social structure of developing countries, where many of these commodities come from small-holders.

3.33 Spring in Yunnan, where rice must follow wheat in a matter of days. The Chinese have developed varieties adapted to specific seasonal light intensity.

3.35 Intermediate technology creates a grain winnower capable of serving family farmers near Chengdu.

- Figures 3.33–3.36, with examples of benefits from scientific research and local skills, suggest that employing 'appropriate technology' is a key to rural progress in developing countries. What may influence government decisions on what is appropriate?

3.34 Simple technology used in Sichuan to provide local farmers with an efficient means of threshing.

3.36 An Indonesian family using traditional hand threshing.

4

$\mathcal{P}$ROBLEMS OF HARNESSING ENERGY

- Fossil fuels: sources of energy and chemicals

- Fossil fuels – environmental threats

- Nuclear energy – advantages and hazards

- Wind and water – more effective uses

- Solar energy – methods of harnessing

- Energy from the ocean

- Energy from geothermal sources

- Developing energy on a local scale

- Energy conservation and recycling

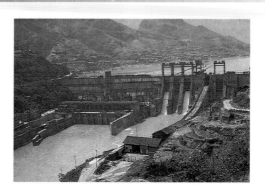

A clean source whose development may involve environmental disturbance.

ENERGY EVERYWHERE – WHICH FORM TO USE?

Transfers of energy, a number of which we have already considered, are involved in every part of the global environment.

- solar energy acting on the upper atmosphere – ozone creation and reactions in the ozone layer;
- distribution of energy received within the troposphere – the greenhouse effect;
- variations in energy absorbed and reflected by surfaces – climatic consequences;
- energy inputs affecting atmospheric conditions, ocean currents, ice cover;
- energy received for plant growth, and plant competition for energy;
- energy passing through food chains and stored, available for use;
- energy released by volcanic activity – local and global consequences;
- environmental side-effects of obtaining energy from fossil fuels – the release of gaseous pollutants.

We need to find practical ways of harnessing as much energy as possible and converting it to our needs without undue damage to the environment. Unfortunately in each case there are disadvantages in using wood, coal, oil, gas and radioactive elements on a large scale, and economic and practical problems in harnessing some of the renewable alternative sources. Yet somehow we have to maintain the requirements of industrially developed countries and raise living standards among the rapidly increasing populations in the developing world. The alternative is a future of unrest and instability. It is also absolutely essential to develop the most efficient ways of using energy, controlling its consumption, and conserving it.

- The increasing demands for 'harnessed' energy can be appreciated by listing details of daily energy consumption by a modern suburban family – at home and beyond – and those which a rural family in mid-Victorian England might have made. Consider then the likely effects of increasing consumerism in developing countries.

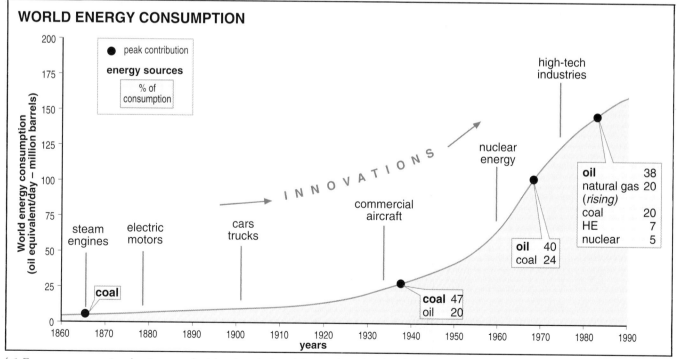

4.1 Energy consumption has increased with urban-industrial growth and technological innovations, and will continue to rise as an increasing population seeks higher living standards. The prime sources of energy have changed, as shown, and many countries use a wider mixture.

Non-renewable energy sources

4.1 shows our dependence on three **fossil fuels**, coal, oil, and natural gas, over a period of accelerating consumption of primary energy – *their* chemical energy made readily available by various mechanical devices. They occur widely across the globe and, although not evenly distributed, can be transported with relative ease. These sources of energy for electricity generation and for internal combustion engines also provide industrial materials, especially petrochemicals. However, on our human timescale, they are non-renewable.

How long will they last?

Workable concentrations continue to be discovered, using satellite surveying among new technical methods. Even so, with growing consumption reserves of oil and gas are dwindling: at current rates recognisable oil resources would probably last 50–80 years, and those of natural gas 70–120 years – whereas coal deposits could provide energy for several hundred years. Such estimates will be affected by the demands of an increasing world population (p.79), boosted by the growing requirements of developing countries. However the constraints of rising costs and problems of extracting and distributing falling reserves must also affect forecasts.

Nuclear energy released by fission (p.64) also relies on finite sources of mined uranium ore, so that **most energy supplies depend on dwindling materials.** Thus it is prudent to harness sources which are continuously or cyclically replenished (renewable) in quantities sufficient to be viable alternatives, and also to diminish demands, and conserve what we've got.

Fossil fuels – individual contributions

Coal was the chief contributor to global energy supplies until after World War II, when, with rising manufacturing and mass transportation, **oil**, with its triple role of providing electricity, fuel for transport, and chemicals for industry, overtook it. As increasing amounts of petroleum were transported across the globe from various oilfields, competition kept the price of crude oil low. Economies boomed on the back of low energy costs.

In the 1970s political disturbances in the Middle East and North Africa **brought the era of cheap energy to an end.** In 1973 the soaring cost of crude

oil pulled other energy prices with it. Recession in industrial nations and debts in the developing world deepened in 1979, when Iraq's revolution and Middle East instability combined to double prices again.

Governments were forced to consider a mixture of energy sources and take conservation seriously. Oil surpluses appeared in the mid-1980s and prices dropped. But the days of relying on cheap energy have gone, and measures to counter environmental threats from fossil fuels are likely to increase costs (p.62).

Consumer decisions affect reserves

The drain on fossil fuel reserves is affected by government decisions on appropriate fuels to meet demands. Some countries with huge reserves may virtually rely on one fuel, as do oil-exporting countries of the Middle East. China has petroleum resources but mainly obtains energy from massive coal deposits. Nevertheless four-fifths of countries use petroleum as their dominant energy source. Ease of transportation and delivery, and petroleum's triple role have much to do with this. However, most large consumers, including the USA, Germany, and UK, draw on a mixture of petroleum, gas, and coal, though Japan is mainly reliant on petroleum imports.

- As petroleum reserves are depleted should we be more concerned over the potential loss of energy or being deprived of a source of industrial chemicals and lubricants? Consider alternative sources in each case.

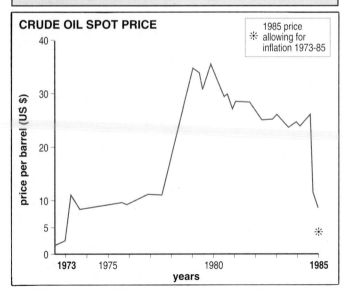

4.2 When the era of cheap energy came to an end.

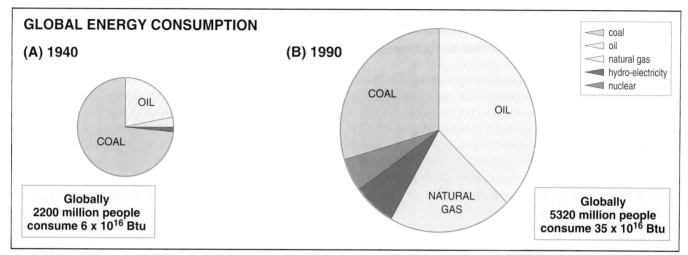

4.3 Energy consumption has more than doubled over half a century, with different sources predominating and the mixture widening.

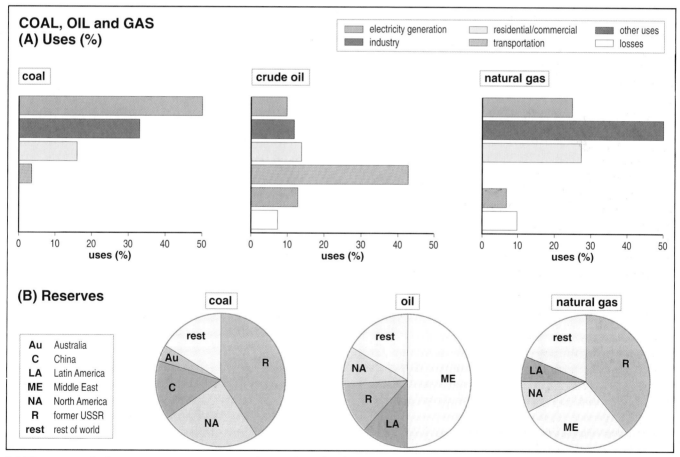

4.4 The uses to which energy sources are put vary (**A**), with crude oil serving many purposes. The strategic location of reserves (**B**) is politically sensitive, especially oil reserves.

Coal

Coal mining with spoil dumps, landscape disruption by opencast working, and storage at transport interchanges is hardly environmentally friendly, but a wider problem is **atmospheric pollution during combustion.** In most coal-burning power stations heat from pulverised coal vaporises water in steam tubes, and the energy of steam-driven turbines is converted to electricity by a generator. Such stations are usually about 37 per cent efficient, for **much energy is lost in the process**, and waste gases emitted include carbon dioxide and oxides of sulphur and nitrogen.

The corrosive potential of sulphur dioxide, its transport as acidic aerosols, and deposition as acid rain make it necessary to control such emissions, even though increasing atmospheric sulphur dioxide to some degree counters global warming, for the aerosols reflect incoming radiation and act as nuclei for water vapour condensation and cloud formation.

The alternatives are to burn low-sulphur coal, use pre-firing to reduce the sulphur content, or employ **flue-gas scrubbers** to absorb sulphur dioxide, at a cost. Scrubbers allow gases to react with a limestone flurry, producing calcium sulphate (gypsum) as a solid removable waste. This further reduces efficiency by three per cent and has attendant environmental problems. It is usually difficult to obtain sufficiently pure limestone within range. In Britain this has meant quarrying areas within National Parks. There is also the problem of dumping excess gypsum. At further cost the waste nitrogen oxides can be made to act catalytically with added ammonia to form water and nitrogen.

For greater efficiency some power stations first transform coal to a hydrogen-carbon monoxide-methane mixture, and remove unwanted sulphur as hydrogen sulphide. This mixture drives a gas turbine, while exhaust gases drive a steam turbine, raising efficiency by about eight per cent. Unfortunately there is inertia in energy generation, and in the short term it may be cheaper to modify old stations than replace them with more efficient ones, especially while new gas-burning ones are built.

Coal provides energy in other ways. Coal gas can be catalytically converted to liquid fuel for vehicles. By liquefaction solid coal can yield crude oil for further refining, and produce methanol as high-octane fuel. As with other oil alternatives, such as biofuels (p.66), the processes involved may be energy inefficient – more energy being put in than is ultimately available for work.

Natural gas

Natural gas is mostly used by producing countries. About a tenth is exported, of which a small amount is liquefied and shipped – though exports should increase with the general trend from coal to gas. **It can be burnt efficiently**, has less sulphur, little residue, and yields over two-thirds as much energy as coal for each unit of carbon dioxide emitted; though there are considerable leakages of methane during extraction and transport. It can also power a dual turbine system along the lines of that described at an efficiency of over 50 per cent.

Oil

The proportion of oil which is used to generate electricity is small (4.4). Oil-burning stations are no more efficient than coal-burning ones, and create similar **atmospheric pollution.**

Oilfields, with their **cluttered environment** of derricks, machinery, storages and refineries are often in unspoiled wildscapes, like the Alaskan Arctic coastland about Prudhoe Bay. From there, raised, insulated pipelines run hundreds of miles southward through territory of seasonally migrating wildlife. Declining oilfield reserves and recovery of oil from oilshales and tar-sands add to areas despoiled by mining. **Tanker spillages** can result in local pollution and damage to wildlife on a scale that needs no elaboration.

A different threat is the potential conflict over petroleum reserves concentrated in relatively few areas, notably the Middle East. Apart from the carnage, the Gulf War created large-scale pollution with undesirable consequences, though far short of media predictions that long-burning oilwells were threatening the Indian monsoon system. In fact closing active oil ports reduced the annually measured sea pollution in the Gulf, despite huge man-made slicks. Interestingly, subsequent rains, moistening organic deposits from prolonged combustion, brought an unusual surge of plant life.

- Consider what might be called 'secondary' environmental pollution by oil . . . that from its refined products.

4.5 A rural landscape about the river Main on the outskirts of Frankfurt, overwhelmed by installations of oil refineries, power stations, major road and rail communications, and satellite suburban development.

- Discuss, using 4.5–4.7, the many reasons why energy production is environmentally disruptive.

- Discuss the advantages and disadvantages of relying on coal as a main energy source: consider bulk, location of sources, environmental impact, efficiency of production, competition, and national security.

4.6 Power stations, cables, and pylons along the river Rhine, near Wesseling, contrast abruptly with intensive farming.

4.7 Open-cast coal mining with good transport facilities has economic advantages, but is environmentally unattractive.

NUCLEAR ENERGY – POTENTIAL AND CONCERN

Potential abundance – public concern

A half-century ago this newly exploited energy source seemed the answer to dwindling reserves of fossil fuels. But **concerns over safety** have acted as a brake to nuclear reactor construction. By the mid-1970s the USA had over 100 of these in operation or under construction, yet made no new orders after 1978. The Chernobyl disaster deepened public concern and political opposition.

Over 400 reactors in some 30 countries produce about a sixth of the world's electricity; another hundred are under construction. Apart from the USA, those with most operative reactors are France, the former USSR, Japan, UK, Germany, and Sweden. Nuclear energy supplies three-quarters of France's electricity and over two-fifths of that in Belgium, South Korea, Hungary, Sweden, and Switzerland. Despite this, there is **a relative standstill in development** which, in view of increasing energy demands, reflects public unease. Sweden is phasing out its nuclear stations.

Energy from fission

Fission describes the break up of the nucleus of a uranium isotope into two fragments which together have less mass than the original nucleus, the difference being **the conversion of mass into energy.**

Mined uranium is mostly a stable form – ^{238}U (whose nucleus has 92 protons and 146 neutrons). Some 0.7 per cent, however, is ^{235}U (92 protons and 143 neutrons). This is so unstable that if its nucleus is struck by a neutron at a certain speed it releases a huge amount of energy and two neutrons. These high-speed neutrons may collide with other ^{235}U nuclei and, if slowed to a speed suitable to cause fission, set up a chain reaction. Appropriate rods inserted into the reactor core control this, and also absorb electrons. A water- or gas-coolant removes heat from the core, which produces steam for generating electricity. Before use uranium is enriched to concentrate the amount of ^{235}U.

A few ^{238}U atoms absorb a neutron and become plutonium (^{239}Pu), which **fast-breeder reactors** use as a fuel – and over a period create more fuel than they consume. High costs of research and operation have hampered FBR development.

Spent fuel elements can be reprocessed to extract unused fuel, but there are few such facilities which means long-distance transport of radioactive material.

With abundant uranium reserves and fewer nuclear stations than anticipated, a costly recycling plant like that of Thorp in Cumbria seems less of an asset.

Nuclear fission – some considerations

- It has the potential to release vast amounts of energy.
- Uranium reserves are finite.
- Nuclear reactors do not release carbon dioxide.
- Initial costs for construction and safety measures are high.
- A large volume of water is needed. Warm water emissions may affect local aquatic systems.
- Safety factors, considering geological faults and population concentrations, influence plant location.
- There are wider fears of major accidents, especially melt-down and vulnerability during war.
- The life of nuclear plant is some 30 years. Shut-down, involving cautious procedures, is expensive.
- Spent fuel elements must be replaced, safely stored, or transported for reprocessing.
- Transport and disposal of radioactive waste, embedded in glassy material encased in concrete drums, are emotive issues.
- Disposal of high-level radioactive waste calls for international agreement over sites for storage, reprocessing, and final disposal. Possibilities of using deep, stable, geologically suitable locations, or ocean deeps, are mostly unresolved.

Nuclear fusion – a long way off

Fusing the nuclei of light elements releases large amounts of energy. To fuse hydrogen isotopes, deuterium (^{2}H) and tritium (^{3}H), whose nuclei repel, means containing the mass of positive nuclei and free electrons in a strong magnetic field at over 40 million °K, so that **energy inputs are very great.** Also it is not 'clean', for it creates local radioactivity. Immense sums have been spent on research and would be needed for further development. As feasibility is not yet certain, this is a controversial issue; many feel such sums would be better invested in developing solar power (p.66) or other alternatives.

- Consider arguments for and against nuclear reprocessing plant which reduces the volume of nuclear waste, increases weapon-useable plutonium, and provides a large national income.

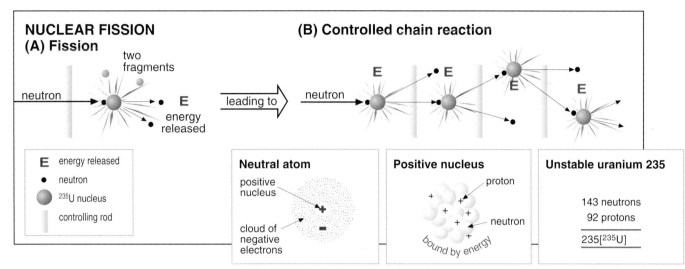

NUCLEAR FISSION
(A) Fission

two fragments

neutron

E energy released

(B) Controlled chain reaction

neutron → E • E E E

leading to

E energy released
• neutron
● ²³⁵U nucleus
controlling rod

Neutral atom
positive nucleus
cloud of negative electrons

Positive nucleus
proton
neutron
bound by energy

Unstable uranium 235
143 neutrons
92 protons
235[²³⁵U]

4.8 Controlled chain reactions in plant which is expensive to install, make safe, replenish, extract waste from, and ultimately shut down.

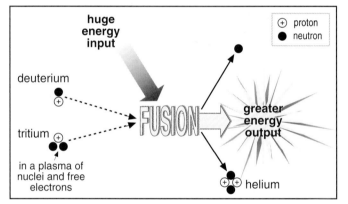

huge energy input

deuterium

tritium

in a plasma of nuclei and free electrons

⊕ proton
● neutron

FUSION →

greater energy output

helium

4.9 (*above*) Immense amounts of energy are needed to effect fusion, which potentially could provide much more. Costs of research and installing suitable technology are very high.

- The pros and cons of the exploitation of nuclear energy are discussed opposite. Give your personal views as to which seems the most persuasive reason for continuing to develop its potential, and which best advocates abandoning it?

- The development of nuclear weapons with potentially serious environmental consequences is another issue. How does it affect the judgements called for above?

4.10 Hinkley Point nuclear station in Somerset takes cooling water from the Bristol Channel. In an area of low population, it is close to the South-West industrial concentrations.

Where small is best

The solar energy reaching earth's surface each year is more than 15 000 times our annual energy consumption. Even the polar regions receive large amounts during summer. In the less developed countries, where small is often best, more and more locally constructed or assembled concentrators are being used to provide hot water and heat for cooking. 4.12 shows a simple type of **solar energy concentrator** used in China. Small mirrors fastened by tar to a concrete slab focus energy onto an iron cooking-grid. A tower type of water-heater is also simple to install.

Solar energy for electricity

For large-scale capture the problems are how best to collect solar energy, convert it to electricity, and distribute it to urban-industrial areas. It can be received by absorptive panels, or focused by banks of mirrors to raise solutions in towers to over 1000°C, and so provide energy for power stations. Location is always a problem, for **the amount of energy available varies** with latitude (4.11), season, cloudiness, and time of day. Sites in hot deserts and semi-deserts have advantages, but may be ill-located for distributing electricity to areas of high demand. This is no problem in southern California, where **'solar farms'** cover many hectares of dry countryside, using black absorption panels winged by mirrors and changing angle to receive maximum radiation during the day.

Photovoltaic cells, with semi-conductor crystals of silicon or gallium arsenide generating electricity which can be stored in batteries, have been used in space-craft. Some countries use banks of photovoltaic cells set at angles according to latitude, to provide local electricity. For wider use there are problems of scale and expense.

Passive heating

Solar energy can be absorbed and distributed through buildings by air currents or a heated-water system. In the widely used **Thrombe system**, sun's energy falls onto a black-surfaced masonry wall behind an outer glass layer, warming the air between. As this rises and passes into a room through a vent, cooler air replaces it through a lower vent. At night the vents are closed and heat radiates inward from the thick wall. In tropical countries sun-orientated black walls are advocated for fuel-saving and the installation of **solar heating panels** is also spreading, notably in India.

Solar energy released by plant matter

Vegetation, the temporary store, can release energy in ways other than coal burning. Biogas generators are in common use. In China a pre-fabricated three-metre diameter concrete cylinder is sunk into the ground and its slightly curving brick roof, with inlet and oulet pipes, made airtight. Wastes from fields, animals, and people ferment and supply methane to homes, and even to power tractors. Treated residues, removed at intervals, are used as fertiliser.

Sugar-cane can be very efficiently converted by fermentation to produce ethyl alcohol. Among other biomass energy sources manioc yields alcohol and water hyacinth yields methane; even bracken, gorse, and wood residues from quick-growing trees planted for coppicing and thinning (p.44) can be converted to fuels.

> The energy flow density of a fossil fuel generator is some fifty times that of bright sunshine (1kW/m²). By comparison harnessing solar energy needs large equipment, raising generating cost. What advantages may counter this? Will a 'carbon tax' help other renewable sources compete?

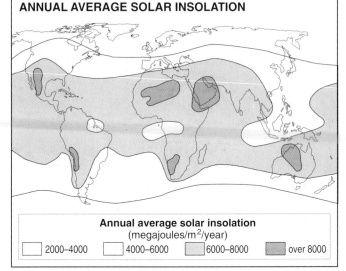

ANNUAL AVERAGE SOLAR INSOLATION

Annual average solar insolation
(megajoules/m²/year)

2000–4000	4000–6000	6000–8000	over 8000

4.11 The solar energy received annually varies with latitude, season, and cloud cover.

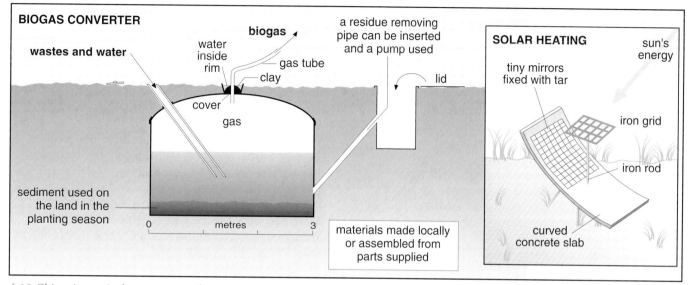

BIOGAS CONVERTER

wastes and water

water inside rim

biogas

gas tube

clay

cover

gas

a residue removing pipe can be inserted and a pump used

lid

sediment used on the land in the planting season

0   metres   3

materials made locally or assembled from parts supplied

SOLAR HEATING

sun's energy

tiny mirrors fixed with tar

iron grid

iron rod

curved concrete slab

4.12 China, in particular, encourages harnessing solar energy and the use of simple converters of local wastes – intermediate technology which can benefit many of the less developed countries.

- Why is solar energy the *indirect* source of much of the energy we use in everyday life?

- What seems to be the major hindrances to a wider use of solar energy?

- Consider why 'small is best' seems appropriate for making the best use of solar energy at the present time.

4.13 Methane from a converter in a Chinese village is piped to a heater set on the old fuel-burning cooker.

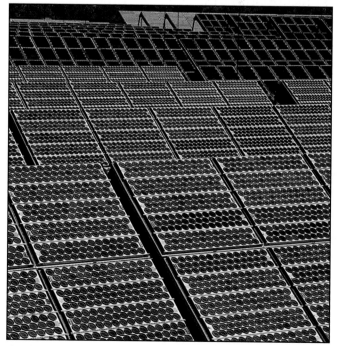

4.14 In contrast to 4.12, a quarter of a million solar cells of a photovoltaic system in Utah directly absorb energy for use or storage.

HYDRO-ELECTRICITY – RENEWABLE, CLEAN, DISRUPTIVE?

Generation at different levels

Water is **a renewable source of energy**, part of the hydrological cycle, being replenished from streams or reservoirs as it flows through generators. The process is clean, emitting no carbon dioxide or other atmospheric pollutants, and may be part of a multi-purpose system, the water passing on for irrigation or controlling river levels.

The advantages depend on scale. In a suitable environment small generators can tap streams to supply electricity at village level, as in the moist, forested hills of south-east China; while water held by a large dam may generate enough energy to benefit millions, though developing such a project may have undesirable social and environmental consequences. The location of huge dams and reservoirs depends on advice from engineers, economists, and ecologists.

Super-dams – advantages/disadvantages

Numerous so-called 'super-dams' are being, or are about to be constructed in developing countries, with the prospects of considerable benefits, despite environmental disruption and social upheavals.

In China **the Three Gorges (Sanxia) Dam** on the Chang jiang (Yangtse river), considered for over half a century, is to be built in the next two decades. The whole project demonstrates consequences relevant to other super-dam schemes.

- A dam 185 m high across the spectacular Three Gorges (4.15) will create a 660 km-long reservoir, 175 m deep. When completed, an HE plant of some 18 million kw capacity will supply the Central and Eastern China grid systems with relatively cheap electricity, **vital to China's expanding economic development**, and from **a clean source.**
- A thermal plant of equivalent capacity would burn 50 million tonnes of coal a year, with inevitable pollution.
- 11 500 tonne ships will be able to serve industrial Chongqing.
- It aims to **lessen flood danger** in the densely populated middle and lower basin, where millions of hectares of cropland can be inundated by floods, like those which drowned 2400 in 1991 (33 000 in 1954).
- Much water will be discharged in summer to remove sediment which would progressively silt up the reservoir, while monitoring flood dangers down-river. During winter clearer water will raise the level. Overall the middle valley will receive controlled clearer water, though this might act to scour dykes. **Reforesting** areas eroded during construction will help prevent material reaching the reservoir.
- As the reservoir fills **about a million people will be displaced**, over half from inundated towns. Nearly a third of the budget is targeted to re-site townships, build roads, provide industrial enterprises and prepare land for rural families.
- **Historic sites** will be submerged. Relics such as rock inscriptions can be removed, but much will be lost.
- **Wildlife habitats** and fish spawning will be disturbed. The Gezhou Dam has already affected sturgeon's up-river spawning, though there is down-stream stocking from fish farms.
- The enormous additional weight of water could trigger **fault movements**, though serious earthquakes are unlikely.
- **Climatically**, a slight temperature increase in winter and decrease in summer should suit local fruit farming, especially the mandarin oranges.

Hydropolitics

After years of debate, China tackles such complexities with some dissension. **Projects on river systems can be controversial.** Turkey's Grand Anatolian Project in the upper Euphrates basin could cut water for Syria and Iraq by over a half. In some cases there are racial as well as environmental issues. Canada's second James Bay project, with 23 power stations, opposes Cree Indian interests. Under pressure Brazil is holding back plans for dams in northern Amazonia which would flood forest-Indian territory; though further south HE developments on the upper Paraná and its tributaries have involved serious deforestation and biocide pollution from newly irrigated areas – consequences exported down-river. In India the super-dams of the Narmada river project will drown forest and farmland, and are being vehemently criticised.

Yet, as always in environmental issues, **a balance sheet must be prepared** drawing up the advantages (of flood protection, 'clean' energy, available perhaps for electric tube-wells or local industries) against the undesirable aspects.

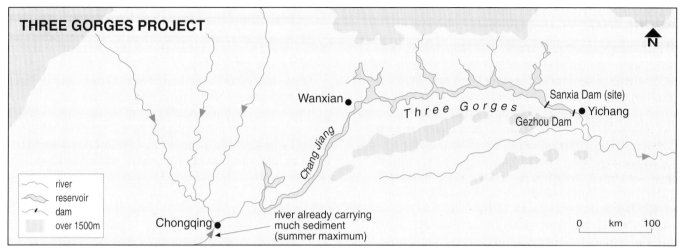

4.15 An immense reservoir will rise between the narrow, steep-sided valleys behind the Sanxia Dam.

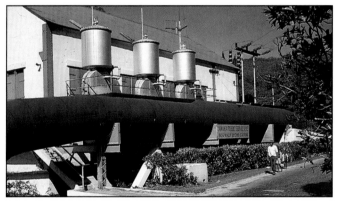

4.16 Jamaica's Bog Walk power station – a small effective source for public service.

- Creating reservoirs to maintain a flow through generators may be environmentally disruptive, but consider other uses to which they may be put and their amenity value.

- List particular physical factors which are likely to be considered when establishing a reservoir and hydro-electric power plant, in relation to the actual site and also the water catchment area.

4.17 At present coal carried along the Chang jiang is a vital commodity for industrial Chongqing. The Three Gorges project will provide energy for its high-tech industries and provide deeper water for shipping.

Wind energy

Wind energy has long propelled ships and created rotary movements to operate pumps for water supply or drainage, or powered machinery to mill grain. In a sense, wind is a second-hand source of solar energy, an inexhaustable supply which can be harnessed to create electricity. Striking aerodynamic propellers on a high tower it causes rotary motion which is transferred to turbines. As wind strength varies electronic controls allow the rotor to turn at optimal speed. Wind generators, grouped in so-called **'wind farms'** can supply electricity to a grid system.

This is **a clean, renewable source**, cheaper than thermal electricity. Capital costs are low compared with thermal and nuclear plant and a wind farm can be installed in months rather than years. The styling of light-weight blades of composite materials aims to overcome **the noise problem**, though this is still disturbing, and the appearance is, aesthetically, a deterrent.

California has the greatest output of electricity from wind farms, with many thousands of generators, and in Europe farms in Denmark supply electricity at commercial rates. The British Isles has Europe's highest potential for wind-power, and is evaluating the feasibility and acceptability of tower clusters in various parts of the country; for instance the wind farm at Llandinam, Wales, with some 200 rotors, has had noise problems.

Theoretically, about a sixth of the UK's electric energy could be supplied by land-based wind generators, though the population distribution and a closely-settled rural landscape make this difficult. Even more could be obtained by establishing offshore 'islands' of generators, visually more acceptable, though at greater cost. The electricity would be fed into the national grid, so variations in output due to fluctuations in wind strength would be lost amid the normal adjustments to variation in demand.

Individual wind generators are used for many purposes. Again, China, appreciating their value for villages and isolated communities, manufactures and distributes mini wind generators of 50–100 watt capacity, suitable for family use.

Wind and waves

Wind energy stimulates wave motion, and waves can be made to act on a large piston to compress and release air, whose surges drive a turbine. This is in use off Norway and Japan, and in Britain a small oscillating column generates electricity for the island of Islay: the seas off northern Britain are most suitable for wave energy systems.

Wave energy can also be harnessed to create up and down movements of floating cams and work hydraulic pumps, and to obtain energy from the compression and expansion of air in pliable containers pounded by waves. The contribution of energy from such sources is small, but the potential of wave motion will remain as non-renewable sources decline.

Tidal energy

The ebb and flow of this lunar-induced motion is already generating electricity on a large scale. Opportunities to develop it depend, of course, on coastal configuration and tidal range.

The tidal station on the Rance estuary in northern France has supplied the grid system for a quarter of a century. Atlantic tidal flow builds up against the Cotentin peninsula to a range of ten metres. Water surging up and down the narrow Rance estuary passes through bulb turbines in a dam near St Malo. In Britain the projected Severn Barrage would close sluices at high-tide to maintain the water-level until the tide ebbed sufficiently for the outflow to drive turbines.

The ocean heat reservoir

Oceans absorb nearly three-quarters of the planet's incoming solar energy. In the tropics there is a considerable temperature difference between the sun-warmed surface waters and the ocean depths. A small **thermal energy conversion system** in the Pacific obtains energy by allowing warm water to vaporise liquid ammonia, which drives a turbine to generate electricity. Cold water, pumped up from several hundred metres down, condenses the vapour to liquid. No pollution is involved. The electricity may be transmitted ashore or used at sea, perhaps for chemical extraction or electrolytic production of hydrogen – a clean, storable source of energy. Incidentally there is research into producing hydrogen at wind farms, as an energy store which could be transmitted more cheaply than electricity.

- Wind turbines need some 200 m spacing which makes farming and energy generation theoretically compatible. Discuss.

OFF SHORE ENERGY GENERATION

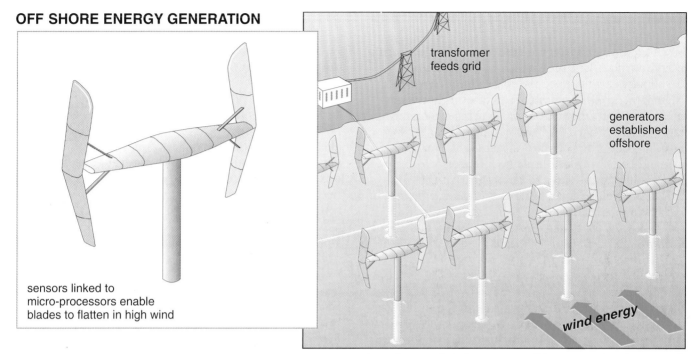

sensors linked to
micro-processors enable
blades to flatten in high wind

transformer
feeds grid

generators
established
offshore

wind energy

4.18 Groups of wind generators offshore may take advantage of unobstructed air-flow, where noise pollution and visual impact are less likely to offend.

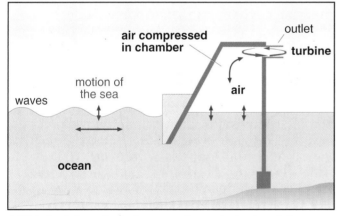

air compressed
in chamber

outlet

turbine

motion of
the sea

air

waves

ocean

4.19 (*above*) A method of compressing and releasing air by wave energy, enabling a turbine to generate electricity.

- How does population distribution influence the means and effectiveness of harnessing these alternative sources of energy?

4.20 Part of a newly installed wind farm in southern Spain.

GEOTHERMAL ENERGY

Energy from the earth itself

There are **immense energy reserves** in the geothermal reservoirs of molten rock which lie beneath and intrude the earth's crust, and in heated rocks about the magma itself. Deep accumulations of hot water, released by volcanic activity or fissuring as hot springs, have long been used for domestic purposes. Yet we have only recently begun to distribute it over a wide area and convert this abundant, if relatively inaccessible, heat energy to electricity. Iceland only began to develop its network of hot water pipelines in 1939. Now bores near hot springs supply water at 86°C to most of the population, mainly in and about Reykjavik.

Various sources of geothermal energy

Low temperature sources, like those in Iceland, occur in sedimentary deposits in many parts of the world. In Hungary they supply domestic heating, greenhouses, and industrial plant.

Natural steam driving turbines to generate electricity was first used in northern Italy in 1904. Since then the harnessing of geothermal energy has proceeded relatively slowly, though now interest is focusing on alternative sources to fossil fuels. One advantage is that it can be obtained with little adverse effect on the environment. Water seeping through semi-permeable layers towards a deep-seated hot crystalline rock or underlying magma source and accumulating in fissures, or in an overlying porous rock, **may be heated under pressure to some 200°C, while remaining liquid**. Some may rise through a natural fissure and expand as high temperature steam, issuing from the vent with a force which can be controlled.

In so-called '**dry steam fields**' high-temperature steam emerges under pressure from numerous vents and is piped directly to adjacent turbines. Groups of small generators fed by 10–15 vents supply electricity to a grid system, as in the large Geysers field in California (4.21). The more abundant '**wet stream fields**' (4.22) contain super-heated water sources which produce steam when the pressure is released by deep drilling. Up to a fifth of the discharge is steam, used for generating electricity, while hot water can be used for domestic and industrial heating, and by de-salination can yield minerals and act as a source of fresh water.

Problems of a wider use

Such **potential energy** would greatly benefit most developing countries, and many lie **adjacent to plate boundaries**, with possibilities of geothermal development (4.23). In a number of them, ground and air surveys have pinpointed locations where power plants now operate – in Mexico, El Salvador and the Philippines for instance. Establishing generating stations involves **considerable capital outlay**, so such projects need careful appraisal and need to be progressive, for extraction from a single source may only suffice for a decade or so. Even with aid and technology from the industrially developed world, there can be unforeseen snags. Deep drilling is not only expensive, it is not always successful.

Iceland, for instance, has not had great success with geothermal electricity generation; yields of steam have proved to be low. In areas of active vulcanicity **seismic movements may disrupt deep bores**, fissures collapse, and deep water sources may change unpredictably. Sulphur dioxide, common to many volcanic areas, can acidify ground water and steam, and rapidly corrode steel lining-tubes.

Energy from water injection

Where there are deep, hot igneous rocks but no evidence of a super-heated water source, it may be possible to **pump down cold water** and **pump up hot.** Near Penrhyn, in Cornwall, the deep granite rock contains about twice the heat found elsewhere at equivalent depth. During research a bore enabled explosives to open a network of cracks in the rock, to accept cold water pumped down. Heated water at 200°C was retrieved from 6000 metres through a separate bore. It proved that deep drilling and overcoming problems of excessive fracturing are very expensive, and it is likely that progressive cooling would allow a life-span of only 25 years or so. Worldwide research continues: deep rocks as yet make only a minor contribution, but are potentially a great source of energy.

- Satellite surveys now evaluate energy flow from ground sources, and monitor the height and nature of volcanic clouds, including sulphur dioxide emissions. Consider the value environmentally.

4.21 Part of The Geysers dry steam field north of San Francisco. Vents are connected to a power plant on the right. Apart from serving northern California, electricity is supplied to Nevada.

4.22 The Wairakei wet steam field – a major source of geothermal energy in New Zealand's North Island.

- Geothermal energy is theoretically available for many of the less developed countries. What uncertainties tend to hamper capital investment in its practical exploitation?

- Locate some of the regions where geothermal energy has provided an environment which brings a profitable income from tourism.

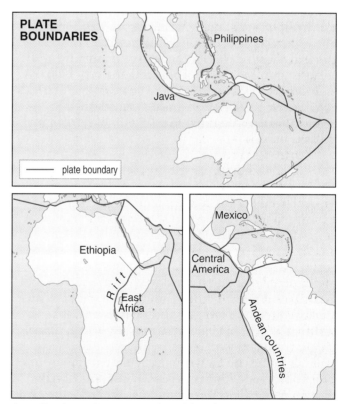

4.23 Geothermal activity, with visible volcanic action, occurs close to plate junctions in, or adjacent to, many developing countries.

ENERGY CONSERVATION

The search for alternative energy sources should go hand in hand with establishing efficient ways of saving energy. It is undoubtedly cheaper to *save* a unit of energy than to generate a unit.

Energy efficiency in industry

Huge savings can be made in introducing effective technology for apparatus in everyday use. In industrially developed countries lighting is a large energy consumer, so replacing incandescent lamps with fluorescent ones, which consume only a quarter as much and last longer, means considerable saving. In industry **high-efficiency engines** with, say, electronic adjustable speed-drives for fans and pumps, reduce energy consumption. Machine-powered industrial processes may be designed to minimise inputs from the machines: for instance, simply making a pipe carrying fluid the most effective diameter could reduce frictional loss and cut energy consumption. **Making processes efficient** could mean finding the optimum area of contact between a catalyst and reagents in a chemical plant, using **automated controls**, or introducing technological developments. An American company began to produce polyethylene for plastics some 50 years ago, then 30 years later found a way of reducing the very high pressure required, cutting energy used by half. Shortly after, a new low-pressure process was adopted, reducing energy required to an eighth of the original consumption.

Energy efficiency in buildings

Apart from lighting, heating must be as efficient as possible. Whatever the heat source, solar energy may be a boost, or variations of the Thrombe system (4.25) should be used to **retain heat gained**. Heat losses can be minimised by thick insulated, or cavity, walls, double-glazing for windows, and insulation for ceilings and roofs. During summer, refrigerators, air conditioners, and other **cooling devices** must be as efficient as possible, and in sunny countries windows might be coated with reflective film.

It all sounds obvious, but there are enormous losses from offices and homes, especially in countries like Britain with so many old buildings. Energy-efficiency grants, or tax concessions may be needed to encourage installation of energy-saving devices.

Transport and energy saving

Apart from pollution control through catalytic converters, **reducing fuel consumption** by internal combustion is essential. There are encouraging signs; smaller, lighter vehicles with more efficient engines, better gearing, precise fuel injection, and designs which diminish aerodynamic drag. But **the increasing number of vehicles is a major problem**. A partial switch from cars to mass transport may slightly reduce energy consumption, but world population growth and social aspirations continue to increase demands for personal transport. Car manufacturers and salesmen encourage rapid replacement instead of emphasising durability, which means higher energy consumption to provide materials, and to manufacture or assemble even more vehicles.

Recycling

The energy needed to provide industrial raw materials, the dwindling reserves, and accumulation of wastes are all incentives to recycle. Scrap generated during manufacture may be recycled, but as material passes through customers' hands the amount re-used drops. Yet making glass, steel, and aluminium from recycled material rather than raw material requires much less energy.

There are advantages in making *high-value* products from scrap. After 'cannibalisation' of cars the steel is available for recycling, and processes which can return it to manufacturers as metal of sufficient quality to be used in car production make considerable savings in energy and cost.

Unfortunately the market cannot always absorb sufficient recycled products to lower the volume of wastes. Effective recycling of domestic waste depends on early separation – paper, glass, plastics, metals – before dumping. This may conserve materials, but not necessarily energy. Urban wastes in landfill sites can, if efficiently capped, supply piped methane as energy for local manufacturing, as to the Bedfordshire brick-making industry.

- List ways in which energy is wasted (i.e. *could* be saved) in a modern urban-industrial society.

- How might the developing countries avoid the energy waste which accompanied the growth of manufacturing industries in European countries (see p. 76)?

4.24 Toronto, where summer heat gives way to a bitter winter. In the high-rise centre many buildings are designed for heat absorption, energy conservation, and, as here, use low shields against down-draughts.

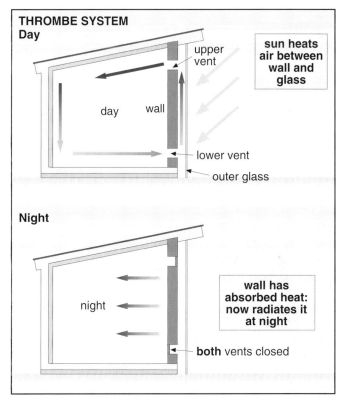

THROMBE SYSTEM
Day

upper vent

sun heats air between wall and glass

day wall

lower vent

outer glass

Night

night

wall has absorbed heat: now radiates it at night

both vents closed

4.25 A system which distributes energy received by day and allows part of that absorbed to be used at night.

4.26 The traffic, street lighting, advertising, illuminated stores, theatres, and cinemas about Times Square are just the visible part of mid-city energy consumption in New York.

Development and energy consumption

As developing countries industrialise, the relationship between productivity and increasing energy consumption is far from straightforward. As European countries, the USA and Japan developed industries and increased productivity, the ratio of the energy consumed to the value of goods and services produced (their GDP) changed from an increasing trend to a decreasing one. They first established an infrastructure based on heavy industry, so energy consumption was high compared with overall productivity. In time, with new technologies converting new materials to consumer goods, energy efficiency improved. There was also some saturation in demand for consumer goods. 4.27 shows how **the energy/GDP ratio progressively decreased** in the UK and Japan.

Energy for the developing countries

Consumer demands of rapidly growing populations in the present developing countries make for increasing energy consumption. This initial surge in consumption might be countered by adopting a combination of technologies, at various levels of society, which use energy as efficiently as possible.

A suitable technology mix should enable them to continue industrial progress at the national level while ensuring sustainable growth for the bulk of the population. China sees it as walking on two legs – the one developing the necessary **high-technology**, the other, aimed at its vast rural population, encouraging highly efficient **intermediate technology**. This is a mix which currently includes the Three Gorges Dam developments (4.15) and the drive to supply affordable equipment at village level.

Some countries face a dilemma: whether to make huge investment in, say, super-dams with a large output, discounting environmental hazards, or to spread investment. A spread might allow smaller, decentralised power stations to supply electricity for rural families, or provide irrigation pumps, or make funds available for improving rural machinery and transport, or for harnessing solar energy to save electricity.

As they develop industries, transportation systems, and buildings, long-term benefits could come from **energy-saving technology**, acquired through financial backing by international organisations **on affordable terms**. Industrially developed countries, anxious to ensure that poorer nations safeguard natural ecosystems, can hardly expect compliance unless they help them emerge successfully from the poverty trap, which is so often linked to crippling national debts.

Choices for the future

Meeting energy requirements for the twenty-first century with environmental safeguards involves judgements which must consider the following:

- Rates of **population increase** in industrially developed and developing countries;
- Over half the world's families use **wood as an energy source** with environmental implications;
- The need to provide suitable **energy sources** for people at various stages of development;
- **Coal:** relative abundance; problems of pollution control; location of reserves in relation to demands;
- **Oil:** facing exhaustion during this period; the consequences for energy production, industrial chemicals, lubricants; pollution control; power politics and location of reserves;
- **Natural gas:** non-renewable; less abundant than coal; efficient combustion; less pollution than from other fossil fuels; location of reserves;
- **Nuclear energy:** a vast potential; high development costs; use avoids fossil fuel pollutants; safety considerations; problem of wastes; association with nuclear weapons;
- **Hydro-electric energy;** considerations of scale; precise location; clean source; high development costs and environmental disturbance;
- Feasibility of developing **alternative/back-up sources;** solar energy; energy from winds, waves, tides; biofuels;
- Problems of **funding research** into new sources and efficient generation.
- **Energy consumption;** how to make large-scale savings.
- **Energy consumption in developing countries is rapidly increasing**, though at present is small on a world scale – the USA's per capita consumption is 12 times that of south-east Asia.

Note that over the period shown in 4.27B the percentage increase in consumption in developed countries was relatively small, partly reflecting reaction to 1970s oil price rises, but from the mid-1980s the rate of increase has been somewhat greater.

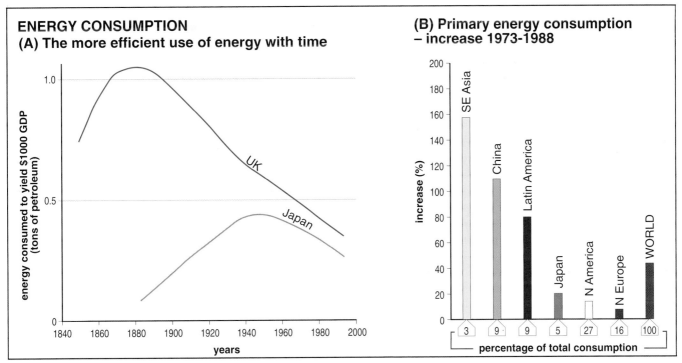

ENERGY CONSUMPTION
(A) The more efficient use of energy with time

energy consumed to yield $1000 GDP (tons of petroleum)

UK

Japan

years

(B) Primary energy consumption – increase 1973-1988

increase (%)

SE Asia
China
Latin America
Japan
N America
N Europe
WORLD

3 9 9 5 27 16 100

percentage of total consumption

4.27 Overall consumption increases with time, but urban-industrial development tends to find more efficient ways of using available energy (**A**)[8]. A significant fact in view of the comparative statistics shown in **B**.

- In view of the fact that over half the world's families use wood as an energy source and that energy consumption in developing countries is rapidly increasing, consider the environmental consequences of failing to provide and fund alternative sources. What forms would be suitable for dispersed rural communities and for those in crowded city settlements (consider the problems of distribution)?

4.28 Fuel and materials for these old potteries near Stoke-on-Trent came by canal.

4.29 The new potteries, with electricity supplying well-lit factory buildings.

5

THE EVER-INCREASING POPULATION

- Population as a potential 'pollutant'

- Contrasting growth rates

- Contrasts in living standards

- Increasing demands – environmental effects

- Subsidising global environmental protection

- Large population concentrations

- Tourist concentration – 'honeypot' pollution

The ever-increasing urban concentration.

PRESSURES ON THE ENVIRONMENT INCREASE

Our need for food, clothing, shelter, and space for waste disposal have always disturbed natural ecosystems, increasingly so as inventiveness boosted demands. For thousands of years disturbance was relatively local, but over the last two centuries technological innovations have enabled us to move and transport materials over great distances. Consumer demands now disrupt environmental systems in far-off countries. The increasing scale and sophistication of our requirements are creating environmental hazards across the globe, and endangering the few relatively undisturbed natural ecosystems.

The development of settled agriculture allowed numbers to increase (5.1A), with concentrations about centres of civilisation. Yet for thousands of years world population rose only slowly, controlled by periodic drought, floods, famines, and epidemics, until the adoption of new agricultural techniques and the industrial-energy revolution, with advances in transport, sanitation, and medicine, initiated a second, dramatic surge of population.

The effects were not immediately universal, but from the mid-nineteenth century the rapid growth of population in industrially developing countries was accompanied by the spread of colonisation. This brought modern medicines, agricultural improvements, better food distribution, and a consequent reduction in the death rate to populations with established fertility patterns, and helped to establish the high rate of increase characteristic of most developing countries.

5.1B shows that by 1830 the human population had reached 1000 million. It took another hundred years to reach 2000 million, but now increases by a thousand million in a *decade* or so. Overall there is a slackening in the rate of growth, but wide variations in different parts of the world.

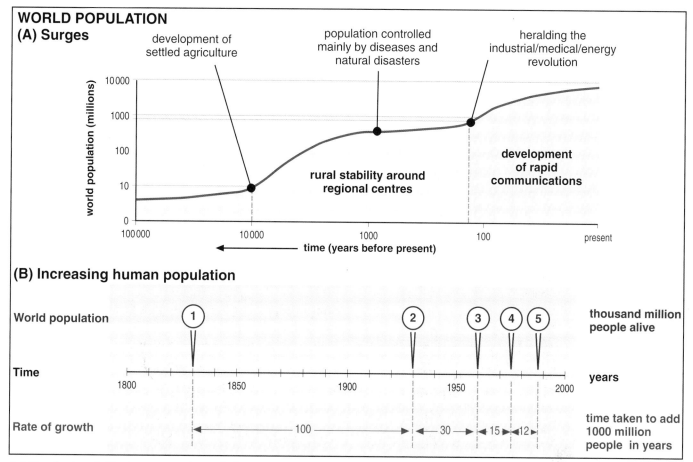

5.1 Developing civilisation saw rural populations grow in response to security and adequate food supplies; yet, remaining at the mercy of natural ailments and disasters, overall increase was slow. Notice the scale of increase following the industrial-medical revolution emphasised in **B**.

THE CONSEQUENCES OF UNEQUAL DEVELOPMENT

Contrasts in population growth rates

5.2 shows variations in mean birth rates and death rates in continental areas over a 35 year period, and consequent changes in the rate of population increase. It contrasts Europe's low rate of increase, where the birth rate continues to fall while the death rate is little changed, with most African countries, where the birth rate remains very high with a significant fall in death rate. In Nigeria, in particular, the population growth rate is still increasing (5.4B).

Encouragingly, among the large populations of eastern and south-eastern Asia a sharp decline in birth rate and continuing decline in death rate puts a gentle brake on the annual growth rate; though even that of two per cent means a huge absolute increase in numbers (5.4A), as it does in Latin America.

5.4B shows the **trend of annual population changes**, with forecasts for the next decade or so. Overall, world population will tend to grow less quickly, though there will be 8000 million by 2025. During the century it should stabilise at about 10 000 million.

Achieving population stability

Initially, as mass-manufacturing brought even modest domestic benefits, the fairly high birth rate increased while the death rate fell in response to more abundant food, better sanitary conditions, and beneficial social legislation. Despite wide gaps between rich and poor, a growing, moderately prosperous middle class, sensing better opportunities for their children, began to opt for a smaller family. Birth control, with modern methods of contraception, despite sectarian religious reservations, has made for a low birth rate. Most European countries are approaching **population stability**, a replacement level of just over two, first achieved by Japan in the 1950s.

Their falling birth rate evolved in a climate of economic growth and high mass-consumption, mostly established when they could exploit world resources with little competition. Besides the European, or European-settled, countries, Japan also benefited from the technology they had developed. These high-consumers maintain living standards with the help of worldwide resources, whereas the so-called developing countries, without these advantages, are unable to progress in the same way. In fact **'developing' is an unsatisfactory term** if taken to imply a similar sequence of industrial development. For most of

them, present economic circumstances make it difficult to raise living standards in this way, or to reduce the high rate of population growth.

Social influences on populations

Four-fifths of the human population lives in countries where social conditions make for a rapid population growth. **For many, a large family has advantages**. In rural communities children do necessary work, and with a relatively low life expectancy a large family may ensure sufficient manual labour, or survivors to perform traditional funeral rites. Socially, old people have the assurance of care. Birth control may be inadequate, due to a combination of poverty, lack of education, religious beliefs, or bureaucratic neglect; though in some such countries net reproduction *is* declining, especially **where women are obtaining better education and personal opportunities**. Otherwise, as available medicines and more adequate food lower the death rate, populations continue to soar.

China, with some 1200 million people, stresses the need to stabilise its population to maintain the recent rise in living standards. Social workers urge families to comply and provide means of birth control. Couples with only one child receive social benefits. The rate of increase has steadily fallen, even though many rural families have not readily complied, for those who now work for personal profit find a large family can mean a greater income.

China has long had the advantage of central planning implemented through bureaucrats. Other countries find it less easy to take effective measures. Latin American countries are hampered by contrasts in living standards and by religious opposition, and India by regional, racial, and religious differences. However, there *has* been a significant drop in birth rates in south-east Asia, though a great numerical increase is inevitable, for the large proportion of young people are tomorrow's parents. By 2025 Europe's population will have a **median age** of just over 40; but in Africa it will be 23 and in Latin America 27, so that stabilisation of world population is a long way off.

- Why is the phrase 'developing countries' apt to be misleading or misunderstood?

- Explain why social improvements, available medicines and more adequate food have contrasting effects on population growth rates in countries at different stages of development.

BIRTH AND DEATH RATES

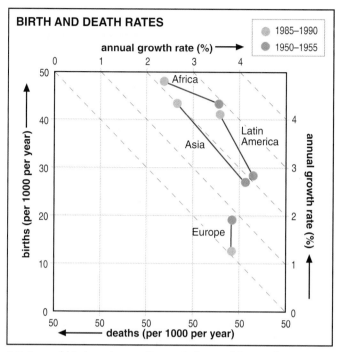

5.2 Annual birth and mortality statistics combine to show contrasting growth rates over half a century – emphasised by the degree of slope.

AGE STRUCTURE – YEAR 2000

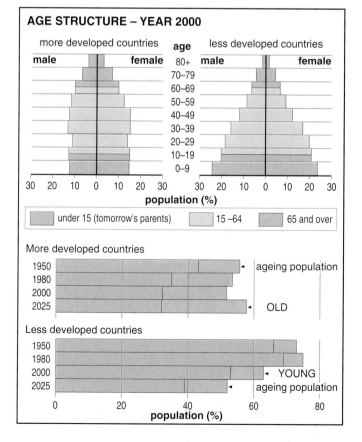

5.4 (*below*) At least the falling growth rate in Asia hints that in time Africa may follow suit; but **A** shows that, overall, the actual increases are huge.

(A) POPULATION

Population (millions):	1960	1990	increase (%)
WORLD	2515	5292	110
ASIA	1667	3313	100
LATIN AMERICA	218	448	105
EUROPE	425	498	17
AFRICA	281	642	128
China	690	1140	65
Japan	93	124	33
Nigeria	51	120	135

(B) GROWTH RATES

— annual average population change
--- estimate

5.3 (*left*) There are marked contrasts in the proportion of really young and ageing members of the population between industrially developed countries and the less developed. The lower diagram hints at problems facing each of them.

'Poverty is the greatest polluter'

Indira Gandhi's assertion is particularly relevant to conditions in many of the less developed countries, where a considerable proportion of the rapidly growing population survives at the expense of the environment. International organisations may urge them to conserve their ecosystem, safeguard natural vegetation, wildlife or historic features, but poverty, ill-health, or inability to escape overcrowded conditions make it difficult for deprived peoples or their government to comply.

Understandably, those without fuel will plunder natural plant cover, those without land, given the opportunity, will attempt to clear and settle, whatever the nature of the soil and vegetation. As the population grows the rural unemployed and landless may be forced to migrate, adding to overcrowded, insanitary shack-settlements in and about the cities: **poverty pollutes**.

Under such pressures governments are unlikely to forego opportunities to use the wildscape for settlement or for forms of land use which will bring in much needed income. Criticism without economic assistance from nations who are measurably better off seems unjust, or can be made to seem unjust. Malaysia's response to criticism of the alleged rate of rainforest depletion highlighted the alleviation of poverty as a priority, and pointed to Europe's loss of natural vegetation and wildlife during the course of settlement.

A reasonable approach to safeguarding ecosystems is the '**polluter pays**' principle. The less developed world sees high-consuming industrialised nations as the main polluters – directly contributing waste emissions, and indirectly putting pressure on the environment through demands for raw materials.

High consumption – the side-effects

5.5 stresses **inequalities in average annual consumption** of people in countries like the USA, Japan, and France and poorer countries in Africa, Asia, and Latin America. In the former, consumption outstrips resources, so materials are obtained from the world at large to maintain lifestyles. Advertising aimed at continuously 'improving' lifestyles accelerates consumption, creating more and more demands: a situation earth's finite resources cannot sustain indefinitely, nor for any length of time as a growing number of the less fortunate strive for equality.

In the short-term such demands have environmental side-effects. Governments of less developed countries may be forced to set aside land for export crops at the expense of small-holders who survive by subsistence farming. Basic foodstuffs are imported, together with fertilisers and pesticides for cash crops. Subsistence farmers are forced onto marginal land, or accept government-assisted migration; as in Brazil (p.46), this may destroy natural vegetation and disrupt unique ecosystems.

High consumption may seem beneficial if it creates markets for produce from small-holders as well as estates. However such produce can be processed, packaged, and sold at many times the amount received by the cultivator. The inequality becomes apparent when the latter seeks to buy the packaged, imported commodity at a local store.

In order to supply the market, the less developed countries borrow to fund related projects, such as dams, power stations, irrigation canals, or roads. Most are in debt to international banks, financial agencies or multi-national companies. Many do not have the resources to pay off such debts.

Loans, debts and environmental improvements

The World Bank and its Agencies promote economic development by lending governments a proportion of the cost of a specific project, at near commercial rates. Its specialists consider likely environmental impacts of such projects, aim to eliminate risks, and monitor them at intervals. However the borrower must safeguard the environment, and much damage comes from cumulative effects of small unmonitored activities.

One possibility is to **remit debts in return for** government action on **environmental improvement**, with similar stipulations for further international investment. As richer countries may have to accept massive debt write-off eventually, this appears an advantageous way of aiding the poorer. As such debts are available at discount from the lender, in bonds which can be traded, some charitable organisations purchase relatively small amounts on **a debt for nature agreement**, and banks are now investing in debt for environmental improvement exchanges – the American Development Bank has large investment in Mexican debt aimed at reducing Mexico City's notorious air pollution by tree-planting.

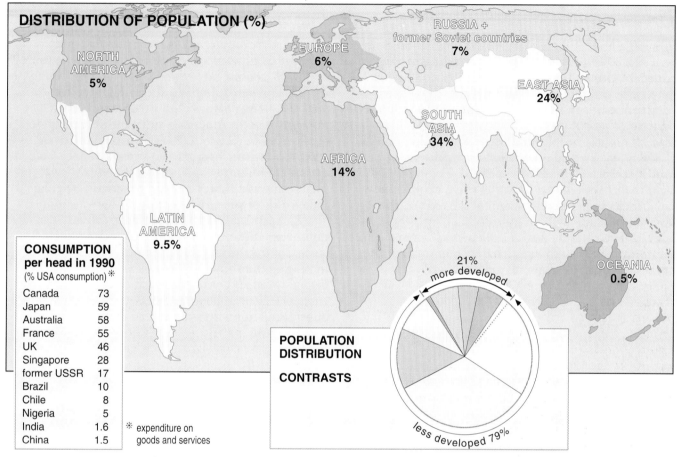

DISTRIBUTION OF POPULATION (%)

NORTH AMERICA 5%

EUROPE 6%

RUSSIA + former Soviet countries 7%

EAST ASIA 24%

SOUTH ASIA 34%

AFRICA 14%

LATIN AMERICA 9.5%

OCEANIA 0.5%

CONSUMPTION per head in 1990
(% USA consumption) *

Canada	73
Japan	59
Australia	58
France	55
UK	46
Singapore	28
former USSR	17
Brazil	10
Chile	8
Nigeria	5
India	1.6
China	1.5

* expenditure on goods and services

POPULATION DISTRIBUTION CONTRASTS

21% more developed

less developed 79%

5.5 Contrasts in population of industrially developed countries and the less developed show that for most people expenditure on goods and services per head is low (indicated by selected examples). The statistics are not strictly comparable in every case, for services provided by a State with rigid central controls are not easily quantified.

- Consider examples of environmental degradation which may realistically be attributed to distant 'polluters', and the justification for expecting help to counter this.

- 'Poverty is the greatest polluter'. 'Advertiser-consumerism has a wide impact'. Consider the appropriateness of these slogans.

5.6 The poverty of Ethiopians in a bare Tigrean countryside, denuded of vegetation yet with potentially fertile volcanic soil, proclaims their inability to improve conditions without aid.

Urbanisation

In 1900 all but a tenth of the world population was rural. **In 2000 half will live in expanding urban concentrations**, some so large that Mexico City will have twice as many people as Australia, that empty continent whose near-coastal urbanisation contains 89 per cent of its population. Ten cities will each have over 20 million people, and whereas in 1920 only 25 cities had over a million inhabitants by the turn of the century there will be 235 of them.

In the less developed countries there has been very rapid increase in the population of large cities, those least able to cope with an influx of landless people and with little to offer by way of skilled employment. The greatest urban growth rates have been in some of the poorest countries – Zaïre, Tanzania, Niger, Bangladesh and Cameroon among them.

Migration from stagnation or disaster

In the less developed countries uncontrolled expansion of great cities has been due both to **high rates of in-migration** and **large natural increase** among the inhabitants. In settled rural areas population increase means that virtually all land available for subsistence farming is taken up and holdings decrease in size. The younger families migrate to the big cities, either directly or via a nearby town. In south-east Asia the majority of immigrants are young males looking for manual jobs at the bottom end of service industries, working as carriers, sweepers, or small traders in competition with thousands of others.

Family migrants tend to move to districts where people from their own region are concentrated and willing to provide shelter and support, overcrowding rooms in existing housing or tenements. Others establish makeshift shacks on the urban fringe, on available sites along road or rail routes or close to an industrial district.

The pull factors, often imaginary, are prospects of employment and better social services, compared with the lack of opportunity and social stagnation in overpopulated rural areas. Every so often a natural disaster or political disturbance may cause **mass-migration** to the city – bringing tens of thousands of destitute homeless to set up rough shelters of available materials around the perimeter.

Improvement of shanty settlements

Communities in illegally-built shacks, lacking sewerage or piped water, may in time upgrade the dwellings, acquire power and water supplies, establish services and small shops, and eventually attract outside commercial and industrial activities. In a number of Latin American cities authorities, under pressure, have recognised **developed shanties as official suburbs**. In some outer parts of São Paulo, a city of 26 million people, authorities provide vacant sites with water, sewerage, and electricity, offering them to those prepared to put up a low-cost house. The city expands with shells of progressive improvement, but receives further waves of casual settlers as it spreads. There is no end as yet to the increasing number of impoverished families sharing dismal social and environmental conditions in such cities as Calcutta, Jakarta, Lima, and Lagos. Subsidising migration can spread environmental damage further afield – as in Indonesia (p.46).

Easing the pressure

It is difficult to combat such urban squalor effectively. Improving specific squatter settlements leaves many homeless people on the margins of society, especially the footloose young with opportunities only for illicit occupations and terrorist backlash, as in Brazil's cities. One alternative is to **check in-migration** by funding projects for employment and improved conditions in rural areas, with measures to control population growth. Another is to provide dispersed industrial centres as foci of settlement beyond the city – like those with electrical-mechanical industries along the Kelang valley west of Kuala Lumpur, in Malaysia.

China has avoided shanty accretions by fostering rural economic progress, with control over migration from the home district, and by developing **satellite industrial centres** about large cities. There is, however, close crowding in high-rise blocks in city suburbs, and problems with young unemployed rural-urban migrants now that restrictions on movements have eased.

- Environmental problems are so often inter-linked. Consider the problems of alleviating conditions described above, while safeguarding natural resources.

5.7 Agra's streets, as with other cities, are thronged with large numbers of men in competition for service jobs . . . pedal-cab drivers, porters, and vendors in numerous small open-fronted shops competing to sell a limited range of goods.

- Consider why rural-urban movements have accelerated in the less developed countries.

- Distinguish between push and pull factors in rural-urban migration and circumstances which may cause one or the other to dominate.

- China was much criticised for maintaining controls over rural-urban movements. In view of the horrific problems of juvenile homelessness in cities like Rio de Janeiro, is there justification for legislation against rural-urban migration? How otherwise might such accelerating movements be diminished?

5.8 Waves of makeshift settlements (barriadas) spread about Lima; yet entrepreneurship gradually effects improvements. Notice the small stores and medical centre, with queue, on the hillside. Suburban services are gradually incorporated.

5.9 Immigrants to Lima's suburbs tend to join those from the home area who preceded them, squatters who have effected improvements. This can reproduce a village atmosphere in the outer districts.

A large city with spreading suburbs is in itself an environmental disturbance, to be contained and controlled. Land communications serving its population and economic activities converge towards urban termini and encourage outward industrial development along their axes. Airports at safe but accessible distances, each a focus of major routeways, extend urbanisation.

Cities as complex organisms

Huge cities in developed countries are in a sense **organisms consuming massive inputs** from world resources, exhaling and supplying energy to their surroundings, **discharging wastes** which need continuous effective disposal, and embodying cancerous areas due to neglect or mismanagement.

Their consumption is maintained by increasing traffic, using dense road networks and causing problems of congestion and atmospheric pollution which, apart from local health hazards (p.22) may have global consequences. Effluents from combustion engines, factories and dwellings produce pollutant concentrations which can be exported downwind for hundreds of kilometres (p.23).

As concrete jungles, large cities affect local atmospheric conditions. In temperate latitudes summer heat combined with humidity is exaggerated in east-coast cities such as New York. During the colder months they create 'heat islands' – reasons why temperature patterns observed by urban meteorological stations should not be regarded as typifying global trends. Within the cities high-rise buildings and narrow streets induce strong air flows – winds funnelling through urban canyons.

Distressing environmental conditions, in particular urban locations, vary from city to city. The indigenous poor and ethnic minority immigrants tend to occupy cheap accommodation in sub-standard properties in nineteenth century decaying inner-city areas, or in unsatisfactory housing estates and high-rise blocks which have rehoused many displaced by inner-city clearance.

Problems of waste disposal

Problems of cleanliness and waste disposal concern the city as a whole. Refuse is commonly transported to landfill sites at a practical distance and at reasonable cost, and as these fill and are made environmentally acceptable, is taken to new sites. At each site leakages through groundwater movement and wind distribution of litter and dust have to be controlled, as well as the gases generated by refuse decomposition. The methane may become an energy source (p.66).

Incineration of municipal wastes emits gases and leaves ash which may be toxic. Many older incinerators in Britain may not meet forthcoming EEC directives on such pollution. Incineration can supply energy to houses or industry, though large investment is required.

In Britain sewage and industrial wastes make up a much greater volume than domestic rubbish, and contain harmful organisms (pathogens) and poisonous effluents, including heavy metals. About a quarter of all sewage sludge has been discharged into the sea, a practice to be totally banned from 1998. Over half is spread on farmland (p.54), but more will have to be burnt, with problems of gaseous pollutants and toxic ash. Sludge may be turned to compost at temperatures high enough to destroy pathogens, and Britain does have plant which incinerate specifically toxic waste, and seeks to increase that capacity. The possibility of profiting by importing and treating such waste is a controversial issue.

A different approach is to produce less waste; reducing packaging for instance, and increase recycling, which would involve greater separation of waste constituents (p.74). An 'environmental subsidy' may be needed, for recycling can be expensive and energy-consuming.

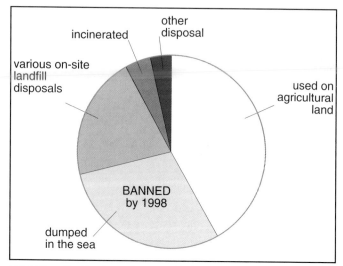

5.10 The distribution of sewage sludge in Britain.

5.11 Lakeside Toronto, a landscape adapted to the demands of a large urban population – railways, motorways, feeder roads, car parks, docks, factories, offices, oil containers, and food storages of a consumer society in an industrially developed country.

- Consider why many families move from inner-city properties to spreading suburbs and adjacent townships, and the environmental consequences of this.

- Discuss why such movements cause problems for private and public transport, and the benefits and disadvantages of urban ring-roads.

5.12 The daily disposal of urban waste illustrates the extent to which energy consumption and environmental damage could be limited by restricting the use of non-biodegradeable packaging material.

5.13 Visual pollution – the clutter of an urban landscape about the dramatic architecture of Köln cathedral – railway, cars, wires, pylons, road signs, advertisements.

TOURIST CONCENTRATIONS AND 'HONEYPOT' HAZARDS

Resorts and centres of interest

People are attracted to a particular place by its scenic, historic, or climatic reputation or its suitability for a given activity. This invariably affects the nature of the place itself, through provision of access, amenities, or accommodation. As holiday resorts develop hotels, cafes, amusement areas, and a host of ancillary services there are benefits and drawbacks for both tourists and local people. The former may enjoy additional facilities yet find initial attractions swamped by development. Local people may acquire sources of income but find their former society and ways of life disrupted. All may suffer the results of over-concentration, with attendant pollution and health problems.

Tourism is a global economic activity which boomed with the advent of cheap mass transport, focusing on resorts served by package tours. Competitive pricing made them available to millions with low and middle incomes. About the Mediterranean, resorts expanded from existing settlements, which initially provided facilities. In southern Spain, tourism at the fishing village of Torremolinos began in the 1950s with a few high-class hotels. When Malaga airport opened in 1962 the whole character of the settlement and coast changed to an extended sprawl of concrete high-rise blocks, with souvenir and fast-food shops. It is worthwhile examining the socio-economic development of tourist venues – the changing numbers, style, and category of accommodation over the years – from a few fashionable hotels to lower-grade ones and self-catering apartments, usually with evidence of growing pollution. This is part of a major industry affecting environmental systems worldwide.

The extension of tourism to **sites in developing countries** leads to social problems: increasing prices of local produce; new life-styles threatening a breakdown of traditional morals; ceremonial practices turned into peep-shows. There are also monetary gains which may benefit foreign companies, supplying most of the produce, and even 'local' souvenirs, rather than the indigenous population.

Parks and nature reserves

Many countries are creating wildlife reserves where species can be preserved and ecosystems protected. They may also serve national interests, as in East African countries who gain greatly from tourism – focused on savannas and their wildlife. Conservationists and park rangers now find it difficult to prevent **environmental damage from tourism**. Camps, hotels, and sight-seeing circuits by vehicles disrupt plant associations and the behaviour of wildlife. Yet financially it is in the countries' short-term interest to increase facilities, and encourage balloon bases, more sophisticated hides, etc.

In Britain's National Parks conservation requirements also conflict with leisure interests and the needs of local people. **Visitors help to destroy what they wish to preserve.** Designated Sites of Special Interest become attractive 'honeypots', with additional carparks, lavatories, and refreshment stalls.

Even where such additions are kept to a minimum, as on Exmoor, the sites may suffer great damage. Dunkery Beacon, 520 m at the highest point, attracts a continuous stream of visitors. This relatively recent stone beacon tops Bronze Age burial cairns. Random footpaths through the moorland are seriously eroded, and about the site the surface has been worn down almost a metre in 50 years, threatening the ancient earthworks. Over 200 tonnes of local stone had to be brought in by helicopter, top-graded and re-sown to preserve the surface, and access restricted to a single track.

Such environmental damage occurs worldwide, from the Egyptian pyramids to historic temples in Nepal. There comes a point where restriction is needed, despite the monetary interests of local and international tourist organisations.

Outdoor pursuits that concentrate participants also threaten the landscape. The boom in golf courses affects access to countryside and water-supplies in dry venues. Ski resorts in Switzerland and Austria replace forest with pistes and access roads, leading to summer floods and mudslides. Water-environments, like the Norfolk Broads, experience bank erosion, pollution by fuel and wastes, wildlife disturbance, and the blemish of tourist facilities.

- Nepal acquires a fifth of its foreign exchange receipts from tourism. The government deplores increasing litter, contaminated springs and decreasing woodland, and urges tourists to bring their own kerosene. The Minister of Tourism applauds new direct air routes and charter flights. This is a conflict of interests typical of tourism. Suggest practical solutions.

5.14 Monkeys and storks scavenge tourist wastes amid Kenyan savanna, with the dangers of transmitting viral infections to wildlife.

- Consider the acceptability of some of the alternatives to mass movements into attractive natural landscape or historic sites, and suggest others. Restrict access to particular viewing positions, or survey from the air?

Establish theme parks or theme centres displaying typical wildlife, crafts, artefacts etc? Forbid public access to large areas of wildscape or ban public amenities therein?

5.15 Benidorm, admirably located on the coast of south-east Spain in respect of sea, sun and scenic highland, with Aitana rising to over 1500 m – now hidden by ever-increasing concrete.

5.16 In the English Midlands people anxious to enjoy the beauty and history of Burton Dassett Hills Country Park litter the earthworks and old beacon with their vehicles.

ENVIRONMENTAL ISSUES — WIDER IMPLICATIONS

Appreciating the complexities

The environmental issues considered in the last few pages show how closely social circumstances and physical conditions are interwoven. We may canvass for what seems an obvious solution to a particular problem yet overlook, or fail to understand, important feedbacks or wider relationships.

5.18 shows a project, developed during the early 1970s north of Wiluna, in Western Australia, to make semi-arid land productive, profitably to produce and market squash, and to provide employment for a considerable number of aboriginal people where few opportunities for permanent occupation existed. But for long periods during the summer the 'shade' air temperature is 50°C, and the rate of evaporation from the many open, lined channels – in which workers stood to cool off – was very high indeed. Within months local stock farmers were predicting a fall in the water-table, justified by the consequences.

Every major activity will have positive and negative environmental influences. An industrial landscape like that in 5.17 can be viewed in so many ways: *negatively* as visual pollution, its factories, transport, and lighting as high energy consumers, its tall chimneys exporting waste chemicals; or *positively* as a praiseworthy example of recycling, a compact, ordered scene of productivity, providing for an urban-industrial society, or supplying the needs of a developing world.

The danger of jumping to conclusions

When considering the impacts of increasing population on earth's atmosphere, oceans, biosphere, or mineral resources, and assessing priorities for our attention and funding, it is essential to appreciate that environmental problems, even local ones, are many-sided, and that apparently obvious remedies may have unforeseen consequences. While it is sensible to be concerned over any potentially harmful issue, it is also important to look behind the slogans and jargon currently used to excite an emotional response. At the global level there are so many uncertainties and, in view of the rapid growth in research and receipt of data from developing technology such as satellites and radar systems, predictions of environmental consequence are continually being revised.

5.17 Industrial landscape in the Ruhr, with trucks laden with scrap metal for steel production.

5.18 Open-channel irrigation for squash-growing on the southern edge of the Gibson Desert in Western Australia.

5.19 A low water table means precarious supplies for pastoral stations in this part of Western Australia.

Glossary

aerosols particles suspended in the air, such as salt, dust, smoke and organic matter

albedo the proportion of incident radiation that is reflected

chloroplast the chlorophyll-bearing receptor in a leaf cell

Coriolis force acts to deflect moving air, with maximum effect at the poles, zero effect at the Equator

ecosystem a complex of soils, plants and animals inter-acting in response to climatic and other environmental conditions

electron a tiny atomic particle with a negative electric charge

epiphyte a plant situated on another in a position favouring its development without extracting nutrients from the host

eutrophication enhancement of nutrient-rich water, causing rapid plant growth

evapotranspiration the combined processes of release of water from aerial organs of plants and evaporation

genetic involving that element of the living cell nucleus which carries and transfers inherited characteristics from parent to offspring

indigenous belonging naturally, native to

ion an atom with a negative or positive charge

isotopes atoms of the same element but differing in atomic weight, containing different numbers of neutrons in the nucleus

leaching the removal of soil substances in solution or by downward percolation

pathogen a disease-producing organism

photochemical reaction between chemicals exposed to radiant energy

photovoltaic radiant energy acts on the junction between two materials to produce electric energy

phytoplankton minute aquatic plants

regolith mantle of loose material covering the underlying rock

seismic related to earthquakes or fault-guided movements

tectonic action affecting the earth's crust

zooplankton aquatic herbivores feeding on phytoplankton, and small aquatic carnivores

Chemicals formed in/released to the atmosphere

chloro-fluoro-carbons CCl_2F_2 and CCl_3F

chloromethane $CH_3 Cl$

dimethyl sulphide $(CH_3)_2 S$

formaldehyde $HCHO$

methane CH_4

methyl bromide $CH_3 Br$

PAN (peroxyacetylnitrate) CH_3COONO_3

(also: oxides of carbon, nitrogen and sulphur, and ammonia)